Marshland

Dreams and Nightmares
on the Edge of London

Influx Press, London

Published by Influx Press
Studio 25, The Heartspace
Hackney Downs Studio, Amhurst Terrace
London, E8 2BT
www.influxpress.com

First published 2013.

Printed and bound in the UK by the Short Run Press Ltd.,
Exeter.

ISBN 978-0-9571693-9-5

To my Mum and Dad, for everything.
And to my Nana, for waiting patiently.

Contents

I	Entropy Junction	15
II	The Memory of Water	27
III	Life Between Epochs	39
IV	A Walk by the River	55
V	The Raving Dead	63
VI	Death of a Fish	77
VII	The Most Peculiar Vanishing of Messrs Whipple and Hazlehurst	83
VIII	Journey to the Rave Hole	109
IX	Temples of the Neo Gods	123
X	The Ghost Factory	133
XI	Biomass	137
XII	Time's Apostates	157
XIII	Ursus Rising	169
XIV	Beasts of the Cryptoforest	175

XV	Marsh Meat	189
XVI	The Rabbit Hole	209
XVII	Behind the Spectacle	215
XVIII	The Fires of London	225
XIX	Endgames	233
XX	The Battlefield	247
XXI	Naja's Ark	255
XXII	Epilogue	271
XXIII	A Dream Life ofHackney Marshes: A Libretto	277
XXIV	Appendix: Soundchronicity Walks	287
	Notes	301
	Acknowledgements	312
	About the author / illustrator	314
	Bibliography	316

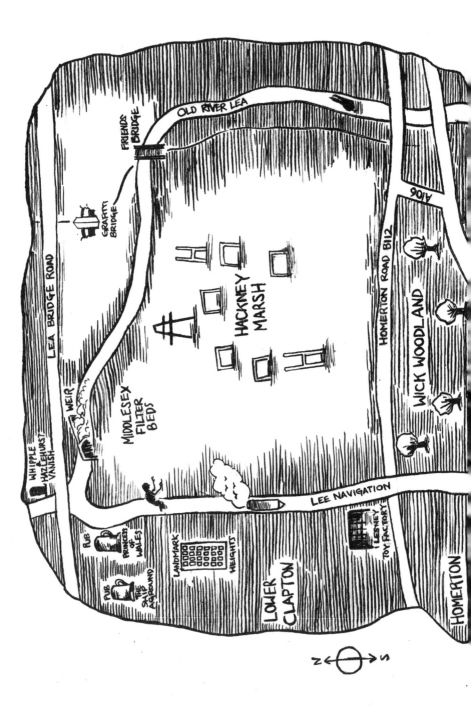

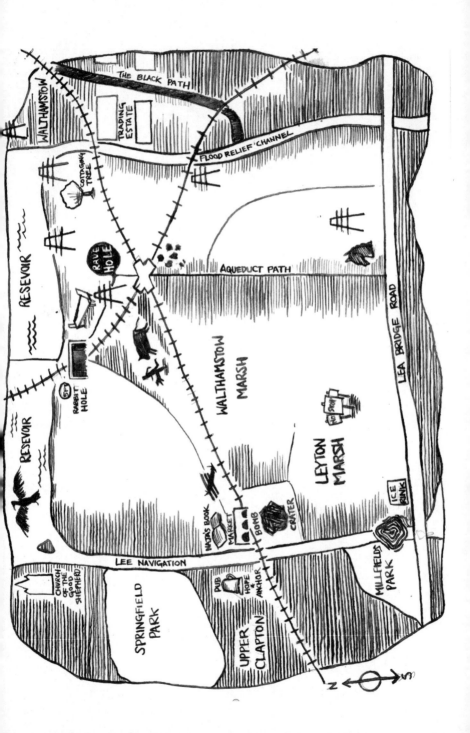

Geography blended with time equals destiny.

- Joseph Brodsky

I do dimly perceive that whilst everything around me is ever changing, ever dying, there is underlying all that change a living power that is changeless, that holds all together, that creates, dissolves, and re-creates.

- Mahatma Ghandi

Men can see nothing around them that is not their own image; everything speaks to them of themselves. Their very landscape is alive.

- Karl Marx, as attributed to him by Guy Debord

One Sunday over The Lea
My boyfriend did it to me
He did it once
He did it twice
Then he had the cheek to say it weren't nice

- Old Music Hall song

Wiv a ladder an' some glasses
You could see to 'Ackney Marshes
If it wasn't for the 'ouses in between.

- from 'The Cockney's Garden', words by
  Edgar Bateman

Marshland

Dreams and Nightmares on the Edge of London

Gareth E. Rees

Illustrated by Ada Jusic

I

Entropy Junction

My first daughter, Isis, was born in Homerton Hospital in November 2008. My parents looked after our cocker spaniel, Hendrix, while we adjusted to our new life. Our ground-floor flat became a cocoon. We warmed bottles and washed muslin cloths. We worked through boxes of congratulatory chocolates. We welcomed visitors and stacked teddy bears in the corner.

We did the parent thing.

When Hendrix returned I realised, with queasy vertigo, that we were a proper family. The sort you see in children's drawings standing next to a house beneath a smiling sun. So it was on a bright, freezing December afternoon that my wife, Emily, and I took Isis out for the first time. We went to Millfields Park on the borderland of the marshland. Daddy, Mummy, baby, dog.

The enormous pram seemed ridiculous as we wheeled it into Millfields. Isis was ensconced in layers of white. All you could see was a pixie nose and her eyes, freshly woken from myopia, taking in the elms passing overhead. I took some photos, feeling like a tourist who had just quantum-leaped into someone else's life.

As we walked down through the park towards the River Lea and the marshes of East London which lay beyond, the city's gravity began to lose its hold and my happy narrative fell to pieces. From the water's edge a shape moved towards us at speed. Though small in the distance, I could tell it was a bullmastiff or some similar barrel-chested Hackney man-dog. I knew right away it was heading for us. It didn't waver from its route, thundering on the frozen ground, growing closer and larger.

Emily and I stopped walking and watched it hurtle up the slope. Hendrix sniffed the grass, oblivious. I removed his lead from my pocket and called him, but it was too late. The dog was upon us. It ground to a halt before Hendrix and the two began to spin. The mastiff's tail, stiff and vertical, quivered with aggression. Hendrix's tail was slung low as he snarled back. A voice echoed across the park as a dreadlocked man staggered towards us with a lead.

I reached out to grab Hendrix's collar. It was like pushing the 'ON' button on a blender. The two dogs whirled into a blurry frenzy round my arm, barking, teeth bared. I staggered back in pain, bitten. Emily cried out, jerking the pram away. The animals were separated but circling again.

'Sorry man,' wheezed the owner in a Caribbean accent, shaking his head. 'He's a puppy. You okay?'

He had a hold of his dog, but it was too late. The idyll was shattered. My family dream exposed for what it was, an artificial construct, fragile as glass. Isis screaming her tiny lungs out. Emily shaking her head in disappointment, me staggering around saying 'shitshitshit'. A scenario which would characterise many subsequent family occasions.

A few months later, I saw them again in Millfields, this time on the Lee towpath. I spotted the dog first. He ran up to Hendrix, chest puffed out, whirls of hot air snorting from his nostrils. Then I recognised the owner. The dreadlocks, the deep vertical lines on his face. He wore a dark blue tracksuit and smoked what was either a rollup cigarette or the last remnant of a joint.

The dogs circled. Mr Mastiff's dog rose up on his hind legs and gave Hendrix a couple of right hooks. Hendrix took two steps backwards and plunged into the river. All that remained on the water's surface was a cloud of dirt. His head bobbed up and he started paddling against the current. He moved absolutely nowhere at first, then backwards as he lost strength.

'Sorry, sorry, sorry,' Mr Mastiff mumbled.

I dropped to my belly and tried to reach into the water. The ledge was too high to get my hands on him.

'My legs,' I said to Mr Mastiff, 'you'll need to hold my legs.'

I piled my mobile phone, keys and loose change on the concrete, lay on my stomach and said, 'Ok – NOW'. Mr Mastiff held my ankles and slid me forwards until I was dangling over the water, clawing at Hendrix's collar.

If I'd been someone else passing by – if, say, I'd been myself on one of my walks – I would have returned home and written excitedly about seeing a Caribbean man in a tracksuit doing 'the wheelbarrow' with a scruffy white bloke on the edge of the river while a tiny dog swam backwards. But I wasn't the observer. I'd become one of *those people* you see doing inexplicable things when you come to the marshes. I'd been exploring the place only a matter of months and already I had been assimilated into the weirdness. For this reason I consider that moment – being dragged back over the ledge with Hendrix, soaking wet – as a kind of baptism.

Welcome to Entropy Junction, the frontier crossing of that borderland between city and marshland, where the competing gravities of two worlds create unusual frissons.

Things happen here.

*

It was Hendrix, a cataract-stricken puppy, jet black and bumbling, who first brought me to this frontier, shortly after my wife Emily and I moved from Dalston in the west of Hackney, to Clapton in the north east of the borough. When he was strong enough to walk the distance, Hendrix led me away from Hackney's Victorian terraces through Millfields Park. I remember the day well, the perfume of freshly cut grass and Hendrix's tiny legs tripping over twigs. We passed a Jack Russell shitting pellets into a shrub. A jogger whooped, 'Yeah!' and boxed the air. Toddlers shrieked on the swings. A drunk lay on a bench, beer can on his belly oozing dregs. A suited man mumbled into a mobile phone. Two kids kicked a football. A murder of crows amassed by a bin. Then, at the bottom of the park, it all came to a halt.

At the River Lea, the park ended abruptly at a tumbledown verge, twisted with weeds and dandelions, iron bollards tilted like old tombstones, chain links snapped. Where you'd expect a towpath to be was, well, nothing. A soup of stone and soil poured into the water. Across the river a concrete peninsula bristled with weeds, empty but for an office chair, traffic cone and a Portaloo circled by gulls. A moorhen stared back at me from a rusted container barge. Beyond the corrugated fencing, geese flapped across a wide sky where pylons, not tower-blocks, ruled the horizon. Near a footbridge, narrowboats were moored beneath a brow of wild scrub. Ruddy-cheeked people in Barbour jackets and mud-spattered wellies strolled across the river, followed by giant dogs, as if a time-space portal had opened up between Hackney and Devon.

This was my first encounter with the marshland. It was a place unmarked on my personal map of the city. Until now I'd perceived London as a dense, functional infrastructure spreading out to the M25. Each citizen's experience depended on the transport connectivity between their workplace, home, and favoured zones of entertainment. Londoners journeyed through their own holloways, routes worn deep into their psyche. The idea of deviating from this psychological map hadn't occurred to me. I assumed I lived in a totalitarian city. London's green spaces were prescribed by municipal entities, landscaped by committees, furnished with bollards and swings. There was no wilderness. There was no escape. You couldn't simply decide to wander off-plan. Or so I thought.

Now my dog had brought me to a threshold between the city I knew and a strange semi-rural wetland known as 'the marshes'. On one side of the river, London was in hyper flux, perpetually regenerating, plots as small as toilets snapped up by developers, gardens sold off, Victorian schools turned into apartments, bomb sites into playgrounds, docklands into micro-cities, power stations into art galleries. Everything was up for grabs. On the other side of the river – a stone's throw away – lay a landscape of ancient grazing meadows scarred with World War II trenches, deep with Blitz rubble, ringed by waterlogged ditches, grazed by long-horned cows, where herons and kestrels hunted among railways, aqueducts and abandoned Victorian filter beds. It was untamed, unchanged in some parts since Neolithic times. It had not yet been claimed by developers. It was nobody's manor.

Discovering this place was like opening my back door to find a volcanic crater in the garden, blasting my face with lava heat, tipping reality topsy-turvy.

*

In that year when Hendrix dropped off the edge of London into the Lea, the riverside was the booming frontier of Hackney's redevelopment. For decades the Lea had been dominated by Latham's timber yard and other warehouses. Now these edifices were being torn down and the skeletons of waterfront flats rose in their place, wrapped in wooden hoardings. Among the graffiti tags, guerrilla advertising stickers and splashes of dog piss, developer's posters envisioned the future in neat lines and diagrams. There was a phone number you could ring to discuss the price of a space in the sky that hadn't been built yet. Above the rim of the hoardings, yellow excavating scoops bowed on hydraulic necks.

A few old warehouses remained on the towpath. Sometimes a figure stood smoking in one of their iron-grilled doorways, ghosts of fag breaks in times past. Signs on the walls said **DANGER, DEEP EXCAVATION**. Beyond I could hear the chugging of the diggers and the crunch of steel on brick. Eventually the wall would come down and a shiny corrugated edifice would rise in its place, reflecting fresh aspects of light onto the river.

Month by month the topography of the river's edge mutated. Gaps appeared between buildings and quickly filled with cones, planks of wood, crumpled sleeping bags and beer-cans. Protective wooden hoardings were built out onto the towpath, narrowing the passage. At times I was forced onto strips of path so slender I tottered on the water's edge to let cyclists past. London was flowing inexorably east, like hot lava, cooling on contact with the Lea, bulging at the riverside, forcing me over. I could feel the city's desperation to burst across and swallow the marshland whole. Some mornings a layer of thick mist shrouded the river's

surface, as if the inert world on the marsh side of the water was sublimating on contact with the super-heated city.

I could see where previous layers of development had cooled, especially by The Anchor and Hope pub, a Victorian watering hole near High Hill Ferry, an old river crossing point. Among the cyclists supping cask ales, jocular men in a hotchpotch of fashions from several eras – bobble hats, donkey-jackets, tracksuits, garish shirts and teddy-boy coats – were dwarfed by a hill of 1930s multi-story flats and newer municipal school buildings. There used to be two other pubs here, The Beehive and The Robin Hood Tavern. They formed a bustling hub at the northern end of Hackney's own Riviera, a popular East End holiday resort. Until the early 20th Century the riverside from the Lea Bridge to Springfield Park enjoyed a festival atmosphere, with crowds, boaters and stalls selling sweets, cockles and whelks. Today it's little more than a narrow thoroughfare for cyclists and walkers. The towpath drops into steep, littered verges of weed, where rats scuttle and swans nest in islands of sludge.

There's something heroic about The Anchor and Hope pub standing firm against time, its drinkers obstructing the commuter flow, while its environs have been fossilised by the pressure of progress. The Beehive was closed sometime after the Second World War, later converted into flats. The Robin Hood Tavern was demolished in 2001. The site was a waste-ground for several years until locals converted it into a community garden. Now a pub sign adorned with an image of Robin Hood and Friar Tuck overlooks a driftwood bench and herb beds. A flyer pinned to the gate advertises 'Folk Dancing'. It's one of many pockets of resistance along the Lea's edge where the past refuses to vanish. Beneath a railway arch, a smiling sun goddess and a green man are painted on Victorian brick. In a plot behind the rowing sheds, a scarecrow watches over the allotments. Latin graffiti daubed on the path by the narrowboat moorings reads *Omnia Lumina Fiat Lux* ('Let there be light'). Beneath a branch overhanging the river a driftwood dragon spins in the breeze. These folklore fragments intimate something wild and primal trying to break through the veneer of modern Hackney.

*

It was the school holidays. The sun was hazy warm. I was crossing the footbridge over the Lea from the marshland to Millfields with Hendrix, absorbed in my thoughts, when I neared a group of young kids milling at the edge of the park. I'm accustomed to bored teenagers in parks, but there was something unsettling about this scenario. They were all male. There must have been twenty boys whispering and jostling in a huddle.

As I drew closer the fog of self-reflection lifted. I became aware something was about to happen. The boys nervously adjusted their jackets. The park crackled with energy. I wanted to turn back but I was too close now. The touchstone was lit. With a whoop, one of the boys vaulted onto his bike and bolted across the grass towards the Lea Bridge Road. The group swarmed after him. I was directly in their path but they flowed past me like I wasn't there.

One boy said, 'We'll come at them from three ways.'

Another reached in his coat.

'Come on!' shouted the lead boy, peddling furiously. The pack began running at a pace. At the railings they slowed and jeered at two figures on bikes who jeered back from the Lea Bridge Road.

Two gunshots rang out. Screams filled the park. The playground emptied. Women ducked their children behind trees. Another gunshot, followed by cheers. The two boys fled on their bikes. The gang fizzed by the railings, collectively deciding what to do next. In the dead silence that followed the final shots, I realised they were probably going to run back the way they came, brandishing weapons. I was the only person wandering in the middle of the park. I picked up the pace, hoping my camp speed-walking would not be considered inflammatory. When I looked back, the gang had vanished under the Lea Bridge.

I checked the local papers. There was no report of the incident. Nobody died. Nobody got shot. It was another leak of dark energy from that fissure where tectonic plates of two worlds grind together in Hackney's molten borderland.

II

The Memory of Water

In a hot room in Singapore on the 6th of July 2005 the President of the International Olympics Committee, Jacques Rogge, announced that London had won its bid to host the 2012 Olympic Games. The British delegation leaped for joy. Meanwhile, a city came unglued. A bacchanalian horde celebrated in London's pubs. Jubilant citizens imagined a future where pleasure-domes rose in the east; where dollars, euros and yen poured into the city's coffers; where specimens of human perfection raced through our streets and fucked joyously for the salvation of humankind in a Stratford neo-village.

Before the hangover set in the following day, bombs tore apart three underground trains and a double-decker bus on Tavistock Square. London fell to her knees and wept. Once again, the spectre of violence tapped on her shoulder to remind her of IRA attacks, the Blitz, the Great Fire, plague pits, Viking sackings, clashing prehistoric beasts, the grinding of the earth's tectonic plates and the lakes of fire that bubble beneath her. This city is a pile of bricks and mortar on shifting sands. We are only flesh and bone. Nothing is safe.

Three days after the bombs, a crocodile came to the River Lea.

It was a peaceful 10th of July, 2005. A group from the Inland Waterways Association travelled by boat up the tidal stretch of the Old River Lea from Stratford to Hackney Marshes. The passengers included Mark Gallant of the Lea Rivers Trust and ecologist Annie Chase. They were making an assessment of the Lower Lea Valley before work began on the Olympic site. As they sailed up the the river, they started noticing weird holes in the river banks.

Holes aside, everything seemed as normal. Moorhens and coots paddled in the waters. A heron preened itself on the bank. A Canada goose drifted across the bow of the boat. Then, suddenly, it vanished beneath the water. In less than a second the bird was gone. All that remained were concentric ripples on the surface. The shocked crew waited in vain for the goose to reappear. Soon it dawned on them.

It was *murder*.

Mark Gallant later told the BBC: 'I felt responsible for these people and I wasn't about to go over and investigate, or get too close – put it that way.' He added: 'Whatever that thing was, it had to be big'

There are many predators in England's waterways. Pikes. Otters. Catfish. Escaped terrapins. But in this case the finger of suspicion pointed to a crocodile. Could such a beast lurk in the Lea?

Journalists from the *East London and West Sussex Guardian* went to find out. Lacking the essential tracking skills of modern crocodile hunters, they discovered nothing. They called on the services of Mark O'Shea, a television herpetologist. After his own investigation he suggested that the culprit could be a discarded pet caiman or 'a large pike'.

Gallant said: 'I'm sceptical about the idea it could be a pike. . . I would've thought if it was a pike, there would have been a bit more of a struggle. The way this thing disappeared was almost instantaneous.'

This story could have died along with the Canada goose. But on the 13th December 2011 the beast returned. Mike Wells was having a cup of coffee with a friend on the deck of his boat when he saw a 'goose go vertically down – in the space of half a second it had gone'. He estimated the weight of the bird to be around 7kg. This wasn't something a fish could pluck from the surface like an insect. He told reporters: 'It was pretty surprising the speed with which it disappeared – and it didn't come back up.'

In the rising heat of Olympic fever, the story hit the mainstream press. A *Daily Mail* headline screamed:

Killer beast stalks Olympic Park as experts fear alligator or python is on the loose.

The *Mail* described whatever was in the Lea as a 'mysterious giant creature'. They reminded readers, 'The number of swans on the river and waterways near the newly-built £9bn Olympic Park is also dropping.'

They were wrong, of course. What lurks in the Lea isn't a crocodile. What was seen in the rippled surface after the goose disappeared was a reflection of those human faces, terrified of what lies beneath the city, wild, ancient and unstoppable. The memory of water.

*

The Thames cuts a lonely swathe through maps of contemporary London. She's one of the last visible remnants of a natural landscape lost beneath concrete and steel. She trails sadly through the megalopolis like a party ribbon hanging from the back of a crashed wedding limousine.

It wasn't always this way. In the past the Thames enjoyed the company of many tributaries including the Fleet, the Effra, the Tyburn, the Westbourne, Walbrook, Falconbrook, Stamford Brook and Counter's Creek. These rivers have been bricked up, turned into sewers, forced underground. The 40 mile long Lee is one of the few to stand firm against the insatiable city as it spreads east. She begins life in the Chiltern Hills at Leagrave, flows South through Ware, Cheshunt, Waltham Abbey, Enfield Lock, Tottenham, Clapton, Hackney Marsh, Hackney Wick, Stratford, Bromley-by-Bow, Canning Town and finally Leamouth where she pours into the Thames.

In the lower Lea Valley the river carves a border between the modern boroughs of Hackney, Leyton and Waltham Forest, and the historical counties of Middlesex and Essex. Between the 9th and 11th Centuries AD, the Lea was the frontier between Saxon England and Danish Viking territory. The Danish Vikings had established a foothold in East and North England in 865AD, carrying out raids on the Saxons, looting villages and stealing livestock. To keep the peace, King Alfred signed a treaty with King Guthrum agreeing a border which stretched from the Thames up the Lea, then up the Ouse to the ancient track known as Watling Street. This border became known as the Danelaw. The Saxons would stay to the South and West of the Lea. The Danes would keep to their patch to the North and the East. The Vikings, however, were a notoriously restless bunch. In 894AD the Lea was wide enough for a fleet to sail as far as Ware in Hertfordshire, their ships adorned with images of dragons, banners bearing ravens, the crew hungry for pillage. Saxon legend has it that Alfred responded by draining lower reaches of the river, cutting off the water channel at Waltham and stranding the enemy.

This was only the beginning of human meddling with the Lea. Over the centuries artificial channels have sapped her strength. She's been diverted through mills, forced into filter beds, hemmed into reservoirs and siphoned away by factories. In the 18th Century the process of canalisation began. A series of cuts and locks aided the transportation of grain and building materials into the city. Like a harpooned sperm whale at the mercy of hunters the Lea grew slower with every blow. Each new drainage channel was a slashed artery leaching her lifeblood. Her wounds filled with silt and her heart clogged with oil spewed from industrial barges. Slower she moved, her vision narrowing, until she was flanked on both sides by timber, concrete and iron. By the end of the industrial revolution, the Lea had been forced into the servitude of London, her curvy lines straightened, her naturally wayward character repressed and conditioned by the demands of the metropolis.

Today the river remains a repository of the city's filth, riddled with faecal e-coli and human effluence. Water from washing machines, toilets and baths in London's many poorly connected homes flows directly into the river. Oil leakage from millions of cars and trucks is washed into the water during heavy rain.

The stretch of river between the Lea Bridge weir and the bridge to the Middlesex filter beds, is one of the most visibly polluted sections of the canal. The oil and shit is joined by a flow of . . .

beer cans   cigarette packets

vodka bottles   hubcaps   flip-flops   naan bread

surgical gloves   pro-biotic yoghurt cartons

party balloons   vomit   shampoo bottles

fried chicken boxes   Styrofoam containers   tyres

nappies   carrier bags   fake tan canisters

shopping trolleys   decomposing rats

In the summer, sewage and duckweed form black pustules on the surface, bubbling in the midday sun, the air curdling with the stench of faeces. The geese, swans, ducks, coots, moorhens, gulls and crows of the Lea aren't put off by this pollution. They're too addicted to the abundant supply of food alongside the parks. People throw bread into the water, scatter crumb trails on the towpaths, abandon takeaways on the grass or stuff their leftovers into tiny park bins. By morning the foxes have scattered the bounty wide. Thanks to a perpetual banquet of processed food, the wild birds are junkies, hooked on white flour, salt and chemical treatment agents, bonded to the towpath by their addiction. They nest among cans, bottles and bags, unheeding of the squalor. Geese stalk towpath users, begging for a scrap, eyes milky with humiliation. These are the tortured guardians of the threshold.

Occasionally, skeletal blue boats with names like *Taranchewer* go to work, dragging rubbish from the canal with a conveyor belt. In the six months before the Olympics 2012, these craft worked on overdrive and the Lea was miraculously cleansed. You could see your face in it – without your face being superimposed with kebab meat and a can of Old Jamaica Ginger Beer. It didn't last. Within a month of the Closing Ceremony a sofa bobbed against the weir among a mush of algae, bottles and cans.

But the Lea is irrepressible. She's not like those other tributaries which submitted to the tide of concrete. She isn't broken so easily. It's at the Lea Bridge weir, where the effects of canalisation are most evident, that something remarkable happens. The Lea splits into two. One part of her flows towards Stratford in an artificial cut known as the Lee Navigation. The other plunges into Hackney Marshes, where she reconnects with a deeper chronology, before the city, before people, when monsters hunted on her banks.

She remembers herself.

The transformation is instantaneous. The water slides down the weir and foams at the bottom of the drop. Thick curls of oxygenated white spin down a green gulley where umbrellas of giant hogweed loom. Trees bow at her passing, trailing leaves in her current. Joyously she flows beneath a cast-iron pipe, twirling round rocky islets, swelling and spilling over muddy slopes. She burbles and bubbles. She breathes again.

Bream, chub, carp, roach, eel, and flounder return to her shallows to spawn. Kingfishers and dragonflies dance on her fringe. Herons, cormorants, coots, moorhens and gulls gather on her rocks. In autumn, teal, tufted duck, and gadwell fly from Siberia and Scandinavia to pay their homage. Dogs crash into her in search of sticks. Fishermen huddle around small fires on her banks and stare at her lovingly.

There are other signs of human devotion to this stretch of river. A kingfisher is spray-painted on the outflow of a flood relief channel where it joins the river, celebrating the return to nature of prodigal water. On a concrete wall nearby, a mutant bird with three eyes and ice cream cone-shaped beak caricatures the degenerate creatures of the canalised Lee. These animal totems have never been whitewashed by the council. They understand that the old river can look after herself. What she wants, stays. What she doesn't want, she forcibly ejects.

When heavy rains come she swells into the trees and shrugs her rubbish onto their branches. When the waters subside she leaves behind a sarcastic parade of blue flags, polythene streamers and bottle-top confetti. The further she flows through Hackney Marsh's woodland of poplars, oak, maple, ash and blackthorn, the more proterozoic the Lea becomes. Her banks get wider and blacker with mud. Dead branches jut from the surface, creating eddies that catch your peripheral vision, as if something has been dragged beneath the water. Trees stagger into her, trunks warped and split. The air clags with rotten vegetation as swarms of midges form question marks. Dock leaves the size of whale tongues flop from forests of nettles. Nature seeps from a deep fissure beneath the riverbed, threatening to subsume you and pull you down into the earth.

As the old river arcs past the site of Dick Turpin's long demolished watering hole, The White House, towards Temple Mills, she runs temptingly clear, sand and stone sparkling on the river bed, geese racing over tendrils of green weed. Here the tarmac footpath ends. To continue walking on the riverside towards the Olympic Park, you must duck through a shaggy tunnel of weeping willow, strewn with motoring paraphernalia: number plates, driving licenses, car log books, and torn MOT certificates. The path ends at a wall of bush which forces you away from the river, up an incline. At the top you stand on the edge of a crossing over the A12, confronted with a view of the

Olympic stadia, flyovers and the Westfield Shopping Centre like a concrete layer cake. Here you straddle a paper-thin border between London's future and that dark, primal memory which flows beneath the city and bubbles, occasionally, to the surface in the Old River Lea.

It's no surprise that it was on this stretch of water that the boat passengers saw a goose killed by a crocodile – a terrapin – an otter – a pike. Whatever it was, it tells you everything you need to know about the Old River. She's the city's amygdale. She's the wild nature threatening to burst through the cracks in our streets. She's the insubordinate river, resisting London's spread, refusing assimilation.

When the human project fails, when London lies in ruins, it will be the old Lea who leads the great river rebellion. *Rise!* she'll cry, *arise!* From Dagenham to Hounslow the rivers of London will burst free from their subterranean prisons, spilling crocodiles onto the streets to feast on the last survivors, engulfing the lowlands, swallowing up old marshes and turning parks into new marshes. Brooks will become streams. Streams will become rivers. Those rivers will connect with each other like re-awakening synapses until they form a single aquatic consciousness. She will remember a time before her humiliation at the hands of humankind, when the waters of the world were united as one, and the land was a lonely continent.

III

Life Between Epochs

Please stop crying. It's time, my love, time to go. Put on your indigo coat. Don't wear your high heels. Wear your flat-soled shoes. Make sure there's plenty of food in the cat's bowl. Close the door of the flat. Come wander through Camden, Highgate, Seven Sisters and Clapton, keep walking until you get to the River Lea. Stop on the towpath behind this derelict warehouse, where mist steams off the water and the moon hangs on a rim of orange at the threshold of dawn.

Can you hear that?

A muted horn sounds. A snare drum engine rattles and a crimson prow pushes into view. It's a narrowboat, woodwork decorated with ornate rose motifs. The roof is piled with coal bags and potted tulips. It glides effortlessly, without wash or wake. Around its bow, mist thickens and billows into white florets. A duck swims into its path and is swallowed up by the hull. Moments later a dove flies from her aft and spirals towards the fading moon.

Shapes shift on board. A man in a fedora hat peers through a telescope. Behind him a stout, floral-gowned woman scrawls on a map pinned to an easel. A capuchin monkey on her shoulder threads its fingers through her hair. The air smells of juniper berries and pipe tobacco. A bass drone pulses. Is it coming from the boat or is it the blood roaring in your ears?

The narrowboat engine cuts. Its wale butts the concrete, releasing plumes of sweet purple gas. The man, woman and monkey are standing to attention, mouths wide open, arms pointing.

I know you're scared, but don't be. Put your hand into your coat pocket. Pull out what you find there. See? It's a passport with matted hemp cover, emblazoned with a crest featuring a chicken embryo and an eye staring from the whorl of a poppy. Gold embossed letters across the top read *Citizen of The Unmoored Manor of Mutating Manifestation*. On the back page there's a photo of a younger you in your white wedding dress.

Please understand. This narrowboat is here for you.

Trust me. Take a deep breath. Step off the ledge.

'Good morning, Ma'am, my name is Breisch,' says the man, helping you aboard. 'Welcome to The Unmoored Manor of Mutating Manifestation. You have officially left British soil. The only law you need obey is the law of UMMM. And our only law is that your own will is the law. And so be it.'

'Eeeek!' says the monkey.

He removes his fedora. 'Yours now,' he says.

Don't be hesitant, take it.

'The lady with the monkey to my right here is Mrs Lizzie Locke. That's Locke with an 'e'. Not to be confused with the lock of a canal. We don't bother with locks on this boat, do we? Ha ha!'

Mrs Locke smiles warmly. Look at her easel. It holds an antiquated map of London. The rivers that fed into the Thames before they were bricked up are daubed with red paint.

'I'm happy to report we've successfully circumnavigated the rivers of Fleet, Ravensbourne, Hogsmill, and Roding to reach you,' she says. 'We await your direction.'

'I don't understand.'

'Here, let me see that.' Mrs Locke gestures at the passport.

Go on, hand it to her.

She frowns. Shows it to Breisch. He brings it close to his nose, as if inhaling the ink. The monkey slaps its forehead and tuts.

'No, we're not mistaken,' Breisch says. 'You're the new Prime Minister elect of the independent municipality of UMMM.' A cheer goes up below deck. 'You have absolutely no powers over any man nor woman, except the possession of the hat – 'he nods at the fedora ' – and the choice of our next destination.'

'May I suggest something?' Mrs Locke whispers. 'The Old River behind Hackney Marsh is nice at this time of year. And as we're here . . . '

'We can stop for a drink on the marshes,' rejoins Breisch, tipping an imaginary glass at his mouth.

What else is there to say? The boat is already pushing away from the concrete ledge. Just say, 'Yes.'

*

The narrowboat ignores the line of the river and swings onto the marshland with nary a shudder at the transition. The grass swells like ocean waves with breakers of dandelion yellow. Eddies of purple buddleia swirl round the hull. As Mrs Locke scribbles on the map with a swan feather quill, she notices your surprise.

'We're taking a short cut between epochs.'

'Ha ha! Yes!' Breisch nods. 'The UMMM changes the tidal maps as she passes – draw quickly, Mrs Locke, draw quickly!'

Mrs Locke whistles through her teeth as the quill scratches. The monkey angrily jabs at the map as if to direct her, but she ignores it.

'Feel how smoothly she rolls through the cracks in time,' Breisch laughs, pulling at the tiller. 'Lovely stuff.'

The dawn has fully broken. Over the marshes to the east the sun is veiled by cloud. To the west the sky is clear over a city that blurs the harder you look at it. The tiny, faded moon clings to the Hackney skyline. It reminds you of an illustration a doctor once showed us. A human egg attached to a fallopian tube. We nodded in vague comprehension. Then he presented us with a follow-up diagram of a curled embryo growing outside the uterus.

'Ectopic pregnancy,' the doctor explained. I'd never heard of it. Never thought it was a danger. Not until you were wheeled through the doors of the operating theatre. Afterwards the doctor said you were lucky to be alive. They'd found it in time. But the 'it' was our first child together and it wasn't to be. His or her doomed life had begun in the wrong place. Our child was a whale born in a canal instead of an ocean. The bad news, announced the doctor, was that there could never be another. It was no longer possible.

That was that. Goodbye.

Days, weeks, months went by where we barely spoke. You went back to work. I opened my reclaimed wood furniture shop. 'HALF PRICE BESPOKE TABLES, CABINETS, BEDS – RECESSSION-BUSTING DEALS' said the sign on the door. At nights we came home, watched television and clung tight to our wine glasses, the only things keeping us from sliding into a deep fissure in the earth. Then one evening we made plans. We sat in the kitchen and jotted ideas onto a sheet of A4. You took the pen because my handwriting was illegible. We laughed at that, the first laugh in god knows how long. Joyously we wrote it all down. Leave London. Go travelling.

Europe. Asia. North America. Live a life of adventure. Explore new possibilities. Live by our wits. And why not? I was a dab hand at carpentry. People all round the world could use a carpenter. You had a TEFL and ten years English teaching experience. Kids always need teaching. There will always be kids. Other people's kids, sure, but it's no big deal. We could handle it.

Together we re-mapped our future.

*

'You'd better go below and say hello to the citizens,' Breisch says. 'They'll be interested and not interested to meet you.'

Go down the steps. Push through the curtain. It's bigger inside than you expect. The walls are lined with old maps. Incense sticks jut from the mouths of gargoyles. A table is filled with steaming, varicoloured liquids. People are deep in conversation. A Ghanaian woman in an orange head-wrap guffaws as a man hunched over a hookah pipe exhales smoke through his ears. A girl in a ball gown with mascara-streaked cheeks sticks Rizlas to a crystal ball. A young boy wears a top hat so large it covers his head and rests on his shoulders. An obese man sucks from a skull through a straw. A transvestite holds the *Financial Times* under her arm. A dapper gent in a tweed suit nods at a woman in a niqab who smokes an ivory pipe through a hole cut in the material.

In the far corner an androgynous waif dances to the drone pulsing from a speaker. In the other corner is what looks like a stuffed bear propped on a chair. On second glance, it shifts, opens its legs, scratches its testicles and grunts in its sleep. Nobody pays it any attention.

They're looking at you. Don't twirl your hair in your fingers, it makes you look nervy.

'Welcome to The Unmoored Manor of Mutating Manifestation,' sobs the girl in the ball gown.

'Oi, Misses, I hear you're Prime Minister,' says the boy, his reedy voice echoing inside the top hat.

For the hell of it say, 'No.'

'That's the spirit sweetie!' says the Ghanaian woman.'Drink?'

She nudges the hookah smoker from his reverie and urges him to pass a crimson bottle down the table. 'Stay a while, sit your skinny bottom down.'

Sit at the head of the table, my love. Take the weight off.

'Glass for the lady!' shouts the dapper gent. The waif dances over to the galley and begins clattering in the sink.

'We were in St Katherine's Dock,' the Ghanaian woman begins, as if you've asked a question. 'We usually stick to the underground rivers but we popped up there for a look-see. Very *posh*.'

'Get to the point,' grumbles the fat man with the straw.

She raises an eyebrow at him. 'We rose like a whale from the water and you shoulda seen the people on their balconies sniffing the air like a pie was burning. Ha ha! Couldn't see us at all. Course, there were a few UMMM folk living there, dotted about, willy-nilly. Came out and gave us a wave. Ha ha!'

The waif arrives with a glass and pours out the steaming liquid. The dapper gent nods stiffly. Take that as your cue to drink. It tastes like beef, vanilla and strawberries. It soaks through the roof of your mouth, up through your nose, then into your thoughts. Can you remember a meal with those exact same flavours? It was the night before I returned to the doctor to check out that headache. You said eat up, eat up, everything would be okay.

You feel bold enough to ask the woman a question, but there's a shout from above. 'Pub-ho!'

'Go on up, my sweet,' she beams. 'You'll wanna see The White

House.'

You go upstairs to where Breisch is peeling his eye away from the telescope and pointing excitedly to a pub by a bridge. Outside, men and women lean on a fence, ignoring your approach. Mrs Locke picks up her muted horn and blows. Green smoke curls from her hair. The monkey sucks it into his lungs as he prances on her shoulders. The horn sounds again. Three men tumble out of the pub door onto the bridge, laughing. They're dressed in eighteenth century garb. A barman comes out, shouting something about money.

'Toss him a farthing, Turpin,' shouts one.

'Toss it up his arse,' says the other, 'then toss the both of 'em in the Lea!'

Dick Turpin swaggers back towards the barman, waving a tiny cloth bag. His two friends hoot in derision. They're about to follow Turpin when they're distracted by a young girl, no more than thirteen years old, face caked in grime, sneaking past them.

'Well, well, well . . . what beauty 'ave we 'ere?' They saunter closer, thrusting their hips and doffing their hats.

'Welcome to Hackney Marsh's lost pub,' says Breisch as the UMMM drifts to a halt. 'I'll get the ales in.' He laughs at your consternation. 'Don't worry about those hoodlums. It's not called The Unmoored Manor for nothing. We'll be out of here in minutes.'

Breisch leaps from the boat and strides to the door, nimbly side-stepping Dick Turpin, who has the barman in a throat hold and is trying to push a farthing up one of his nostrils.

'Minutes,' Mrs Locke shrugs. 'Hours, days, years, aeons. Don't make much difference, Ma'am. You know them crappy energy-saving light-bulbs you get, like the one in your flat? Time is like one of those. A coil. You can skip up and down the coil. Around it. Inside it. Whatever you like. You can touch any point at any time.'

'How do you know what's in my flat?'

'My dear, is that really the first question you want to ask?'

'And what question might that be?' booms Breisch. Remarkably, he is now standing right next to you with a tray of beers. You and Mrs Locke take one each.

Be polite. Hold the beer, but don't drink it. I know you don't like beer. You used to tell me it tastes like cabbage.

'We'd better go before Turpin gets a whiff,' says Breisch.

The two men on the bridge stare vacantly at a fish in the water below. But Turpin swaggers towards the river's edge, sniffing.

'That damned scent,' he says. 'Somethin' in the air. Somethin' awry. Somethin' . . . not . . . RIGHT!'

Turpin leaps from the bank as if to board the boat, but the UMMM has pulled away and he plunges into the water. As The White House vanishes behind a bend in the Lea you hear the spiteful laughter of Turpin's friends on the bridge echo back and forth off the membrane of time.

*

Something in the air. Something awry. Something not right.

That's what you thought when I returned from the doctor that afternoon. I waved away the offer of wine and slumped onto the sofa with a magazine I didn't bother opening.

You had classes to teach. That was why you couldn't go to the appointment with me. But why would you have gone? Neither of us thought my problem was serious. Work stress headache. Migraines. My mother had those. It was probably that. Almost certainly so.

Then I took you by the hands and said, 'They want me to do more tests. For a tumour.'

That was the first time you went on one of your walks. You came alone to the marshes. Here you could leave all your problems in a pile on the towpath and cross to another world.

But this marshland you see around the Unmoored Manor is very different to the one you know. It is transforming before your eyes. Hackney Marsh billows like a bed sheet in the wind. Pylons sprout like spring daffodils. Geysers of rubble burst from the earth. Saxon soldiers emerge from the riverbank. With a whoop, they begin to run, waving shields and axes, kicking up the clod with their boots. Among them skip girls in daisy chains and moustachioed footballers in baggy trousers

'Faster, Breische!' shouts Mrs Locke.

The boat picks up speed as it enters the Lee Navigation between Stratford and Hackney Wick. The high-rises and stadia of the Olympic park pixelate and fragment into cubic swarms. There's an eruption of street life alongside the canal. Horses, buses, pigs, trams, cows and cars swarm together. Rows of bored City commuters ride on the backs of cattle herds. Sheep-faced cars honk at oncoming trains loaded with coal. Birds flock over flaming industrial chimneys. Great slag heaps rise beyond blackened factories and cranes bristle against the sky.

The Unmoored Manor groans and tilts, as if rocked by silent explosions. You tremble with fear. Breische ushers you to sit down next to Mrs Locke. 'Prime Minister, Ma'am, as we pass through time, it might become a little rocky.'

'What's going on?'

'A minor skirmish,' says Breische. 'Don't worry. We make no war with London – nor anybody for that matter. But she doesn't recognise our independence.'

The bear sticks its head through the curtains.

'Not now, Mr Moxley!' says Mrs Locke. The bear shrugs and

withdraws.

The Unmoored Manor is roaring up the Navigation, through Homerton toward Clapton. The prow lifts in the swell. You hear calls and shouts from the city. The clang of steel on steel. Cackling laughter and death screams from plummeting factory workers as bombs rain from the sky. Music hall piano chords crescendo with a choir of children. Water-jets arc over the East End of London, forming rainbows as they catch the light.

As the UMMM bucks and rolls, the outline of the city you know disappears under layers of history, each one thicker and denser until the world is a kaleidoscopic swirl and a million voices are singing, screaming, shouting, groaning, pleading, begging, raging, dying. Slumped over the wale, exhausted, you stare into a Lea that's getting older, wider and swallowing everything up.

It's too much. Too much for you, my love. Shout something to Breisch. Make it stop. Take off your Prime Ministerial fedora and scream, 'ENOUGH!'

*

'I love you,' you said to me with a sense of finality as I lay in my hospital bed. You'd seen it in the films. Those neat and tidy endings. The tears, the hand-holding, the significant last words, the eyes closing in death.They'd prepared you for the worst when you'd come to the hospital that morning. My fingers were so cold. But I didn't die. I languished for months, barely conscious, unable to recognise you, dosed up with drugs to stop the pain.

You left me in the hospital. Got on with what you had to do. Gave notice on a two bedroom rented flat you couldn't afford without my salary. Sold my furniture shop for a pittance. Some developer wanted to turn it into a café. I'd not made a profit for a year so most of the returns went into my company debt. The remainder bought you six months' rent in a tiny ground floor apartment. After that, well, you had no idea. No sheet of A4. No plan. Nothing.

You moved in with a single bag of clothes. Stocked the cupboards with cat food. Then it stopped.

I died and it was over.

It was all over.

*

'I said ENOUGH!'

'As you wish, Ma'am.' Breisch heeds your anguished cry, cuts the engine. Bracing herself, Mrs Locke clutches her monkey in one arm and her easel in the other. The narrowboat steams to a sudden halt, sending glasses and bottles flying below deck. A mass groan goes up.

'Sorry,' you mumble. But you're relieved as the world rushes back into focus. You can make out branches on the trees by the Lee Navigation, sharp against snow, the landscape a cracked mirror. On the opposite side loom three stained tower blocks. People in scarves, flared trousers and parka coats are gathered outside by the car park, chattering excitedly among police cars with flashing lights. A group of men hold gardening forks and point across the water. Are they pointing at you?

Catch your breath quickly. Look out at the marsh – there! Police marksmen stalk the woodland with rifles, dogs straining on their leashes. Helicopters buzz over the playing fields, blowing ice showers from the treetops.

'This again,' sighs Mrs Locke.

The bear's head re-emerges through the curtains, eyes moist.

Breisch reaches down and ruffles its fur. 'There, there, Mr Moxley. You're safe with us.'

Moxley gazes up at the helicopters and roars mournfully. Tutting, the monkey holds a finger to its lips. 'Shhhh!'

'Not sure we want to stick around here long neither,' Mrs Locke says. '1981 was one of them years, weren't it Mr Moxley?'

Vigorous nods from the bear.

'They didn't find you last time, Mr Moxley, won't find you this time,' Breische says. 'But better get down below. Someone's clocked us. There's always bloomin' one.'

A boy in a woolly hat among a crowd by a nearby footbridge stands with mouth agape, staring directly at The Unmoored Manor of Mutating Manifestation. He raises a trembling finger. With a snort, Mr Moxley ducks below. Breisch turns the ignition switch and returns to the tiller.

'Ma'am?' he says, smiling at you.

Tell him you want to go home. He'll know what you mean.

As a helicopter rises menacingly over the treeline and the boy leads a crowd towards the waterside, The Unmoored Manor of Mutating Manifestation lurches forward with a clunk, reminding you of that time you gave me a driving lesson because you were sick of chauffeuring me around. It was an embarrassment you said, a man of my age. There we were with horns behind us blaring, me stamping on the clutch as if it was on fire, our Peugeot 205 kangarooing down Camden Road, your face the colour of beetroot.

That was the first and last time we did that.

Remember?

The narrowboat lurches a second time. Doves whirl in a tornado of steam around its aft. With a *wooooosh* you're pulsing away at speed from the woodland, looking behind at the dark flames of police marksmen in the mist, glowing, flickering, dying.

*

'So we've come full circle.' Breisch's voice jolts you awake. 'What next?'

The Unmoored Manor of Mutating Manifestation is by the weir on the Lee Navigation, engine ticking lightly. Look beyond the towpath. See Millfields Park with its electricity depot, dog-shit bins and basketball courts. It looks like modern Hackney. Your time.

The monkey on Mrs Locke's shoulders is pointing at something and hooting, 'Ooh, ooh'. A poster is taped to a lamppost near the bridge. Under a grainy photo of a woman leaning against a tree is the word MISSING. That's a picture of you. I know, it doesn't feel like you've been away long. But that's how things are.

'I don't know what I'm supposed to do.'

'You're still Prime Minister,' says Mrs Locke. 'You have the hat.'

'Ma'am, she means you can still choose our destination,' Breisch says. 'Anywhere you like.'

'May I suggest something?' Mrs Locke whispers. 'Camden Lock is nice at this time of year. Or any time of year . . . last year . . . ten years ago . . . *fifteen* years ago . . . ' She winks.

Remember the day we moved into our Camden flat. I smashed the glass coffee table as I carried it in. You called me an idiot. We argued. Then we made up, kissed and opened a couple of cold Cokes from the Londis where the people seemed very friendly. We sighed at the enormity of it. Everything we owned was before us in a pile of boxes, waiting to be unpacked and re-discovered.

Uncanny. That was about fifteen years ago, come to think of it.

It dawns on you.

'To the Regent's Canal!' You place the fedora on your head and straighten your indigo coat. I always liked that coat. It's the coat I remember best.

'It's over the weir we go, then!' says Breisch. Mrs Locke draws the monkey down from her shoulders and cradles it in her arms, cooing gently.

The Unmoored Manor of Mutating Manifestation circles at the weir's edge, swallowing moorhens in its mist, engine whinnying, silver doves flapping from aft. You expect to plunge over the foaming lip into the Old River Lea. But the bow of the narrowboat turns instead to face the park.

'Aren't we going over the weir?' you ask.

'Not *that* weir!' laughs Breische. 'Hold on!'

The lamppost with your face on it trembles. The concrete slab at its base begins to crack. The post pulls free and rockets towards the clouds, trailing a shower of stones. The towpath disintegrates. Trees and chunks of concrete fly skywards. A vast cavern opens up. Water cascades into it, drawing the narrowboat to the edge.

It's time to go. Close your eyes. Feel that rush of icy air hit your nostrils. Listen to my voice, I'm speaking to you. *Come back, come back to me, my love.*

The world falls away in the roar of a wave.

Isn't it beautiful?

IV

A Walk by the River

It was 8am on a Sunday. An unusually early hour for me to walk Hendrix, but I'd suffered a night of restless toddlers and awoken beneath my desk with excruciating backache. I wanted to get out of the house before my daughters commenced their sleep-deprived caterwauling. Some days I wonder, who are these little people I have invited into my home? What are they doing here? When are they going to leave?

It was sunny but my head was foggy as Hendrix and I passed beneath the Lea Bridge and approached the filter beds. There were no people around, but plenty of birds. Too many for my liking. Two geese stood sentry in front of the weir. A cormorant perched on the footbridge, eyeing me beadily as I approached, refusing to budge. I paused, eyeing it back, fearful that it was about to launch at my face and peck out my eyes. When I stepped right up to it, the cormorant took off with slow, sarcastic flaps.

When I reached the towpath I saw the corpse. The upturned belly of a swan drifting in the current while a suspicious huddle of mallards watched it pass. What the fuck was going on? Everywhere

I looked, birds gambolled and cavorted, high on petrol fumes and Sunblest. Swans hissed at Hendrix. A coot surfed drunkenly on a scab of duckweed. A gull waddled by, laughing like Joe Pasquale, utterly unbothered by my presence. Two moorhens rutted on the path. Behind them a crow with a can of Coke in its beak ogled them dirtily. When the crow saw me it tilted back the last dregs of the can and flew across the marsh with a contemptuous *waaaark*.

I'd stumbled onto the tail-end of a degenerate avian party.

This is what centuries in the service of the city have done to the river. Bricked her up, hemmed her in, polluted her with chemicals and processed food, populated her towpaths with depraved birds, filled her with human junk. A swan corpse is only one of many disturbing objects I've seen in the water. An armchair, a cluster of children's party balloons, a door with a poem scrawled upon it. But no sight unsettles me more than that of the Lea's footballs, a recurring motif on this waterway. Branded club balls. Plastic balls adorned with Spiderman or princesses. Punctured semi-spheres like skulls after a hammer attack, yellow orbs like sinking suns, obsidian spheres and dead moons. Limp leather sacks with psoriatic skin. Shrunken balls coated in slime. Each one signifies an aborted game played in a garden or park along the length of the Lea.

A child's voice hollers. 'To me, Paul, to me!'

An awkward foot hits leather. Air whistles. Water sploshes. A chorus of groans.

'Paul you dickhead!'

When I look at a ball I wonder how long ago it left Paul's foot and soared over the fence. Last week? A year ago? Longer? If someone can work out the atomic half-life of a football, we'd know for certain. Perhaps Paul is now an old man, slumped in his armchair, wondering where his life went wrong, thinking of that fateful day he booted the ball over the fence. Perhaps he plays for Arsenal and wakes every night in a cold sweat, remembering the jeers of his friends. His entire career is an attempt to rectify his mistake but he *knows* that ball still exists somewhere on the Lea, festering like his shame. Perhaps Paul is still a child, only a more cautious one. He skips school sports these days. He reads poetry instead. His friends still call him a dickhead. He'll get over it.

Footballs in the river speak of failed hopes and forgotten childhood. Once you start noticing them, it's hard to stop. The more you notice them, the more they appear. It's when I'm at my lowest emotional ebb that I see the greatest number, making me wonder whether it's events in my life, or the *balls*, which are the cause of my turmoil. Sinister messengers of the cosmos, they bob against the concrete, ticking like clocks, counting the passing of time as they wither away.

Then I found the safe.

It was lying on the grassy verge of the towpath, a steel cube tilted at an angle, door facing upward. It had not been there when I walked by the previous day. Now it was here. How could that be? Who had left it here? What was inside? My mental Rollerdex flipped through the possible contents: cash, severed head, bomb. Perhaps all three. I scanned the towpath but there was nobody around. The narrowboats were silent. A mallard watched from a distance, head cocked. A swan cut towards me from the opposite side of the Navigation. I tried to ignore them as I bent down to inspect the safe. The door wasn't sealed, but when I gave it a light tug it didn't spring open. I stepped back, sweating suddenly, paranoid with the mallard and swan staring at me. I knew full well what these birds were capable of. This could be their doing. It could be anyone's doing. In the marshland, beyond the surveillance cameras, there was a limitless capacity for a strange and unexpected death. The bodies of executed gang members, murder victims and decapitated circus bears have been found here. What next?

Hendrix sniffed at the door. Panic set in. This was ridiculous. I should just open the door then go about my day. Nothing ventured, nothing gained. This was what being a writer was all about, looking behind the door, taking a risk. But I couldn't. All I could see was my shredded flesh spraying across the Navigation in the aftermath of an explosion, Hendrix's severed head spinning up into the air, crackling like a Catherine Wheel on the overhead power lines. *It's jammed*, I told myself. *I don't need to get a crowbar to know that it's jammed. If it could be opened it would be open already. I can't possibly be the first to have seen this. The dog needs walking. I've no time for this. Someone else can stare into the jaws of death.*

I called Hendrix to my side and walked away, disgusted with myself. I had thought myself immune to that manufactured fear of abandoned bags, slow-dripped into our collective consciousness by the government and its media cheerleaders. But it was apparent that I had an innate dread of the city in which I lived. I was as brainwashed as the next person. Curse the bastard who left that safe there, forcing me to confront my weakness. I scowled at a swan on the towpath. *And don't think I don't know what you're up to.*

Tormented, I crossed Hackney Marsh to the Old River Lea, where I could leave behind the footballs, junk and demented birds. Surely I'd find consolation among the ancient mud banks, spawning bream and tidal swirls? I was wrong about that, too. There's something about the Old River Lea that stimulates the reptilian brain, hardwired to fight or flight. As a pigeon flapped from a tree, I tensed. A twig snapped. Then another. What was that scuttling in the undergrowth? A lizard? A rat? Some undiscovered species? Was it following me? A dragonfly darted from a forest of nettles and hovered in front of my face. To my crocodile mind, these creatures were predatory apparitions from a different time. I moved quickly along the river bank.

On the top of the incline, a man broke cover, lurching with tilted gait, arms stiff at his side. He wore John Lennon glasses and a raincoat, despite the sunshine. There was something unsettling about the way his haircut – the lank, angular curtains of a 1970s British Rail ticket inspector – contradicted his Peter Sutcliffe beard. It wasn't right. He was like a composite of people I half-remembered from public information films when I was a child. To compound my unease, the strains of ELO's 'Mr Blue Sky' crackled through the foliage from a radio in the warehouses on the far side of the river. I followed the man for a while, keeping myself concealed, ducking behind a tree whenever he turned around. Eventually he took a sharp turn into the woodland and lumbered across the open marsh.

As I watched from behind a bush, I thought to myself: *yes, for certain, that man is some kind of weirdo stalker.*

Walking deeper into the woodland I came across a group standing in the trees. I couldn't believe what I was seeing. African women in bright kaleidoscopic head-wraps stood in a semi-circle. The men, dressed in white robes, formed an inner circle, holding wooden swords outstretched, tips meeting above the head of a girl, perhaps ten or eleven years old. They waited silently for me to pass, smiling. I smiled back but couldn't think of anything to say. I wasn't even sure they were there. They were figures from the dreams of another. I had become a bit part in the dengue-fevered fantasy of a sick city.

These are not the only weird encounters I've had in the woodland between Hackney Marsh and the old Lea. Walking here one day, I saw an ambulance parked in the trees. A body wrapped in a blanket was strapped to a stretcher on the ground. The crew stood by, talking with no apparent urgency. I looked at the victim lying there in his neck brace. His eyes were bright and curious, following me as I passed.

Up ahead was another ambulance. Men loaded a body into the back as dozens of paramedics emerged from the trees with blankets and medical kits. Further beyond was another ambulance surrounded by bodies, either lying on the ground or marched through the trees on stretchers. There was a festive atmosphere, medics flirting with medics, someone cackling loudly at a joke. It was like witnessing a catastrophe on nitrous oxide. My head flushed with panic until it dawned on me that this must be a training drill for Sunday League football injuries.

This is what it's like, certain days, on the marsh.

On one such day, a man appeared round the bend in the path by the old river. He was in his late 50s, tubby, with knobbly hairless legs. Wires protruded from patches on his chest and arms. He looked like a poorly made robot, huffing and puffing as he sped-walked, hips wobbling. As he drew close he pointed at my dog, struggling to speak. 'Hendrix,' he said. 'Hendrix.'

I was startled. I'd never seen this man before. How could he know my dog's name? He stopped, bent over, a string of phlegm oozing from his lips. Then again he said, 'Hendrix!'

'Yes it is,' I said.

'What?' He seemed surprised.

'That's his name.'

'Hendrix?' He staggered towards Hendrix arms outstretched. 'Have we met?'

The man ruffled my dog, letting him slurp his hairless flesh.

'He's Hendrix alright. Same size. Same colour 'n everything. I can't believe it.'

He told me that he bought a black cocker spaniel, many years ago, and they named him Hendrix. 'He was wonderful. A bit mad. We used to come here with him. I think I've seen your dog before on the marshes. I always wondered.'

Hendrix was dead now, but the man was alive, just about. 'I've started coming back to this place again,' he said. 'I had a heart-attack last year. It was touch and go. Doing a bit of walking to stay . . . well . . . y'know.'

When we said our goodbyes, I couldn't shake the notion that this man was me twenty years from now. My moribund future self had just encountered a ghost of his dog, remembering the time he used to come to the marshland and walk by the river. I wondered if that vision made him – well, *me* – happy.

I hoped it did. Poor fucker.

V

The Raving Dead

LOADING...

MY COMPUTER GROUND TO A HALT ONE OCTOBER EVENING.

TWITTER WOULDN'T UPDATE.

VIDEOS ENDLESSLY BUFFERED.

WHAT A NIGHTMARE.

I PUT ON A COAT AND WENT DOWN TO THE MARSHES.

ON THE LEE TOWPATH I WANDERED PAST NARROWBOATS, THEIR WINDOWS DARK...

IT LOOKED LIKE A MAN WITH DREADLOCKS...

...BUT AS I DREW CLOSER I SAW THEY WERE TENDRILS OF WEEDS...

VI

Death of a Fish

The first time I stood in the Middlesex filter beds I recalled a journey I took across Latin America in 2003, from the southern tip of Argentina to Mexico City. Hitchhiking through Tierra Del Fuego in Patagonia I came across the teepees of Ona Indians abandoned by the roadside, so beautifully intact it was hard to believe they'd been abandoned over eighty years ago, not the previous week. Months later, on the twisting trail to Machu Picchu in Peru I was surprised by the ruins of garrisons on the Incan road. These administrative outposts were as beautiful as the altars to the gods in the famous city beyond. Up in the forests of Guatemala in Central America, the restored temples of Tikal were stunning, but more exciting were those still entwined with the forests. They seemed as 19th Century archaeological explorers must have found them when hacking through the jungle.

The thrill of discovering the Middlesex filter beds surpassed those experiences, because Hackney was the last place on earth I expected to be confronted by such a sight. Inside its gates was a network of stone ramparts, split and crumbling, their sloped brick walls crawling with vines. In the centre was a giant stone circle, like a sacrificial altar, scarred with radial furrows and surrounded by broken Victorian pulley systems. The abandoned beds bristled with grass. Green parakeets flitted through a forest littered with rusting containers and sludge pipes, overlooked by a pylon.

I'd lived in London for ten years without knowing of this place's existence. Now Hendrix had led me into a lost world.

In the 1970s paranormal investigators formulated a 'stone tape' hypothesis, speculating that rocks, walls, pottery and furniture could absorb the memory of emotional events and store them for playback. Could this have been the reason for my tingling spine as I caressed the leg of a sluice gate? Humans from two centuries had carved lines into this landscape: rails for sand trolleys, machete scars on tree trunks, trenches for iron pipes. I imagined I could stick a finger in these grooves and play back history like a vinyl record.

Time in the beds doesn't progress in a linear fashion. It's in a perpetual remix. The filter beds are a nature reserve where trees and plants are allowed to grow only so far. When vegetation begins to swallow up the brick and concrete, teams of volunteers hack back the vegetation and burn it in pyres. The environment is kept in an overgrown state suggesting a time five years after an apocalypse. Nature cannot claim dominion. The sluice gates and tiled walls are not permitted to crumble. At the tipping point of nature's reclamation the teams move in with machetes. And so the filter beds remain an accident victim kept forever in a coma, a living memorial to themselves.

In the northern corner of the beds by the weir is an installation by artist Paula Haughney. 'Nature's Throne', known locally as 'Hackney Henge', consists of large granite blocks circled around a stone throne. These are the recycled foundations of the demolished pump house. Until 2013, the south western corner hosted another artwork, 'Rise & Shine Magic Fish'. Ceramic fish heads and tails once rose from the shimmering water of one of the filter beds, gigantic and alive with colour. Then the pump broke. From that day on, the fish gambolled in ocean of grass. Each time this grass was macheted, the plinths on which they rested were crudely exposed. Then the fish seemed like statues built to appease those aquatic gods who once decided London's fate at the hands of cholera and typhus.

One morning I came by this bed to see a fish missing. Only one head and two tails remained. My stomach lurched as I rounded the corner. On the grass by the gates to Hackney Marsh a ceramic jaw bone lay amidst shattered fragments. I crouched down and touched it tenderly, half-expecting it to be fleshy and moist. It seemed as if the fish had been dragged from the pit and devoured on the bank, leaving only its most unpalatable bones. I wondered about the bears and crocodiles sighted in the marshland over the years. How little did Londoners realise that, while they were tucked up in bed, battles between phantom beasts raged beneath the pylons and poplars.

The death of the fish spelled the end of an era. In summer 2013 they transferred the remaining fish to the Essex filter beds, privatised for its own safety, shielded behind ticketed gates. Solemnly I wondered who were the new gods who would protect us now? Perhaps the last hope was that statue of a river god resting by an urn outside the Coppermill Water Treatment Works in Walthamstow, the place that assumed the Middlesex filter beds' role after 1969. This piece, sculpted by Joseph Theakston in 1809, once sat in the original East London Waterworks site in Old Ford lock, a genius loci for London's aquatic infrastructure.

Perhaps there is no longer a need for divine protection. The Middlesex fish have gone. So too has our fear of death by dirty water. The defunct Victorian filter beds have been repurposed for the appreciation of nature. In the Essex beds, birdwatchers peek from hides. Processions of squawking children clutch fact sheets. I too walk the ramparts of the Victorians' crumbling water temple with my dog, watching his urine dribble into the cracks, wondering which of London's current architectural wonders will suffer the same fate: replaced by new ideals, abandoned to nature, fenced and signposted for tourists, fetishised by urban explorers, artists and psychogeographers with books to write.

VII

The Most Peculiar Vanishing of Messrs Whipple & Hazlehurst

Life was most satisfactory until I met Octavius Whipple. Ask any person whom I know and they will tell you, 'Harvey Hazlehurst is a contented man with a handsome wife, a regular wage and a flair for the industry of water filtering.' Except you cannot ask them anything, and neither can they tell you anything, for everyone I know is dead.

The children, grandchildren and even the great grandchildren of the people I know have withered to dust, and the blame lies entirely at the feet of one Octavius Leander Whipple. It fails me to tell you precisely how or why, for I don't understand the physics, but I implore you to believe me – this is most certainly the case.

I am – or, should I say, was – the Chief Supervisor of the Middlesex Filter Beds by Hackney Marsh. Whipple, a new employee of The East London Waterworks Company, arrived on the 8th of August 1861 for a tour of the site. I was mystified as to why they did not ask me to be his guide, being employed in the very week these beds were commissioned and working here every weekday since.

Rumours preceding his arrival told of Whipple's role as a British diplomat who, for reasons unknown, had been forced to return from Paris to London under a cloud. The East London Waterworks Company recruited him to liaise with commoners protesting our purchase of Lammas Land, seconding him to the Essex and Middlesex beds to observe operations. Company director, Mr Graham disregarded my obvious qualifications for the task and took it upon himself to show Whipple around.

Even from a distance Whipple cut a peculiar figure, lanky and clad in purple velvet, a yellow silk handkerchief clutched in one hand and, in the other, a cane with which he prodded the air as he spoke. His red top hat was buckled in the middle, the like of which I had never seen outside of the Punch and Judy show I watched once with my children on Mare Street.

Mr Graham and Mr Whipple emerged from the Pump House where they tarried a while, deep in conversation. I was keen to introduce myself but I was oiling a sluice gate and believed it would reflect poorly on me if I abandoned my work. I coughed emphatically to garner their attention and Mr Graham duly raised a hand to acknowledge me, while Whipple waved his handkerchief and yelled, 'Woohoo!' in the most extraordinary manner, more like an owl than a man. I was even more astonished to see them turn on their heels and depart without so much as a *by-your-leave*.

The following day Sam the messenger delivered me an envelope, inside which was a letter which read:

Dear H.H.,

Please accept my most sincere and humble apologies for my premature exit yesterday. I was called away on urgent business before I could properly introduce myself to your good self. I have been informed of your steadfast character and wish to congratulate you most heartily on your role in ridding this doomed city of disease, for the time being at least.

If it so pleases you, I will meet you by the gates at midday tomorrow when I would be honoured if you could escort me on an authentic tour of your estimable facility.

Yours, for what it is worth,

Octavius Whipple.

What an execrable missive! What was so wrong with my name that Whipple could not bring himself to spell it out? He appeared to suggest that the facilities of the East London Waterworks Company offered no permanent bulwark against disease and that our noble city was doomed, which was utterly preposterous.

Despite my vexation I waited for Whipple at precisely midday, then for many minutes thereafter as the sun shifted on its easterly course and it became apparent that I had been rudely snubbed. When Sam wandered past I said, 'Tell me, have you seen Mr Whipple today?'

'Saw 'im outside The Ship Aground earlier this morn.'

The public house, indeed! I crossed the bridge to Ashpital Dock, doffing my cap to familiar faces, hardly expecting that it was possible Whipple was still within The Ship Aground. Yet I was amazed to find him in the musty darkness at a corner table with two men, one with his head slumped on the table and the other sat stiffly upright in his chair, jaw hanging open, as if deceased.

Whipple was younger than I had initially presumed, perhaps only five or six years my senior, with cadaverous pale skin, obsidian eyes, and a beard speckled with foam, like a ragged sailor recently returned from Cape Horn. I shook the letter at him.

'What is the meaning of this, Sir?'

'Ah, good morning H.H!' Whipple slid a clay pipe from his pocket.

''Tis morning no longer, and if you couldbe so kind as to refrain from addressing me as H.H. My birth name is Harvey Hazlehurst.'

He kicked a chair towards me as if to indicate I should sit down, an offer which I refused.

'Very sensible,' slurred Whipple. 'A man should stand as often as he can on his two legs for it is – more or less – what makes him human. Of course, you are aware of Mr Darwin?'

''Tis some nonsense about monkeys,' I said, slamming his letter on the table. 'You stated clear and plain that we were to meet at noon.'

'So we shall, so we shall.'

''Tis almost forty five past the hour!'

'Truthfully?' Whipple squinted at a watch fob. 'Well strike me down. Father time has again shown himself to be my adversary. Damn him. Damn him to death.'

'No apology, Sir?'

'I apologise most profusely,' Whipple bowed his head. 'Mr Darwin would consider me an animal which has failed to adapt to civilisation's most rudimentary requirements.'

'It bodes ill to place all your trust in what you read in a book, Sir.'

'Precisely!' cried Whipple. 'This is why I have never bothered myself with that insufferable tome, the Bible.'

Choked with outrage I exclaimed, 'Does Mr Graham know you speak in such an impertinent manner?'

Whipple reached across to the man who was slumped on the table, grabbed his hair and lifted up a face which I recognised to be that of Mr Graham. There was drool on his chin and a red circle

where his flesh had been pressed against a farthing.

'Do not fret, H.H.' Whipple lowered Mr Graham's face onto the table. 'I may have lured him into a drink too many. He shall be right as rain tomorrow, likewise Mr Ackart.'

I examined more closely the features of the second guest and realised, with sinking heart, that it was John Ackart, spokesman for the Lammas Defence Committee. At last I understood Octavius Whipple's version of diplomacy. Who knows how many dignitaries, business leaders and politicians he had seduced with alcohol and other toxic potions? Most likely he had the entire upper management of the East London Waterworks company racked up in his pocket like clay pipes.

'We shall reconvene tomorrow at the beds for my grand tour,' declared Whipple, banging his cane. 'Same time, same place. We can discuss – I know not – water or some such nonsense. If I am honest 'tis of little interest unless applied to a fine malt.'

I thundered out of The Ship Aground, angrier about my powerlessness than of Whipple's misdeeds. I was destined for a life of toil as a loyal servant of Empire but the likes of Whipple believed they could do as they damn well pleased.

*

I was less surprised – but no less infuriated – when Whipple failed to appear at noon the next day. Controlling my tumultuous emotions, I returned to the beds where I toiled for a good half an hour. When he finally arrived I was much taken aback for, in place of a hat, Whipple wore layers of white bandages, lending him the appearance of an escapee from Bedlam.

'It pains me to sound like a pedant,' said Whipple as he approached, 'but I understood we were to meet at the gates?'

'At noon.'

'Yes indeed, noon,' said Whipple. 'So 'tis not noon now?'

'Noon passed a good hour or so ago.'

'Excellent.' He shook my hand vigorously. 'Then the matter is settled.' In close proximity I could detect a perfumed odour wafting from his head bandages.

'I have the most terrible ache in my cranium,' was his only explanation.

So began a humiliating tour of the Essex and Middlesex Filter Beds, throughout which the barely suppressed mirth of the workers pursued our every step. I explained the delicate process of modern water filtration but Whipple was disinterested in the details and only slightly more interested in matters directly relating to his role in the Company. As if to compound my humiliation, he insisted I accompany him to the riverside where, gasping vociferously, he unleashed an arc of bright yellow urine.

'I find it most disconcerting to think the fine ladies and gentleman of London will later drink this,' he said, as I averted my eyes.

'As I explained, Sir, the water is taken from upstream and made sanitary before distribution.'

'We are tethered to the system now,' he continued as if I'd never spoken. 'One man's piss quickly becomes a thousand men's poison when it gushes from a pump in Soho.'

After our tour I expected Whipple to remain in whatever dark pub corner he liked to carry out his devilish business, but in this assumption I was gravely mistaken. I saw him every day thereafter, strutting the towpath, lurking in the beds and ingratiating himself with the workers. Oftentimes he wandered aimlessly across Hackney Marsh, scribbling in a notebook which he produced with a flourish when something caught his eye. I was certain that if I were to wrest that book from his grasp I would see nought but doodles of barges, birds and flowers – or poems about clouds. Most exasperatingly, nobody else was as perturbed as I by Whipple's behaviour.

'Mr Whipple's a queer fellow,' said engineer Phillips. 'But 'e's got our best interests at heart. As long as I get paid I aint got no quarrel with nobody.'

'Ne'er a bad word to be said about the man on this day nor any other day o' the week,' said Sam the messenger. I knew not what he meant, for Sam was an idiot, but it was evident that Whipple had commandeered their minds through bribes or beer, or both.

Then he came for me.

Strolling home across the marsh one evening, I spied Whipple's red and white hat poking above the long grass and altered my trajectory accordingly. Alas, he spied me and sprang to his feet, waving his damned handkerchief.

'I have been observing the most extraordinary insect phenomenon, H.H. These ants move together like one mind and yet I know not whether this idea pleases me. Still, they are ants and we remain ourselves. We are not like them, are we?'

'Nor they like us.' I said. 'If you do not mind, Sir, we had to drain one of the beds today. I am weary and wish only to return home.'

'Then of course I shall be pleased to accompany you.'

I could think of nothing to deter him and, besides, Whipple was already beside me, swinging his cane, whistling tunelessly. With every ounce of my being I willed him to desist but he continued all the way to Temple Mills where he finally announced, 'I have a great thirst suddenly.'

Thus it came to be that Whipple was sat in my home, on my

special chair, eating my bread and drinking my ale. He looked like a giant grasshopper hunched beneath the low beams. My mother, almost totally blind, reached from her rocking chair and traced his face with her hands, muttering something about how she felt great life in his beard. What was she talking about? The very idea! My wife Lizzie, blushing, ushered our two daughters towards him and made them sing 'Twinkle Twinkle Little Star'.

'Wonderful, this is all wonderful,' beamed Whipple.

'Look, Sir,' said Lizzie. 'I also make jewellery!'

'I do not think Mr Whipple will be interested,' said I. There was a vogue in the city for cameos, lockets and brooches made from human hair. Lizzie had taken it upon herself to replicate the fashion but, whereas the hair in the popular jewellery was embedded within gems, precious metals and porcelain, Lizzie's versions were *purely* hair – knots of hair, strung onto loops of hair, and attached to more hair.

'Please let me see!' roared Whipple, banging his cane.

Lizzie pushed me in front of Whipple as if I were a child. She grappled at my shirt to reveal a necklace fashioned from her locks, interwoven with strips of gay ribbon.

Whipple leaned forward. 'You are quite the dark horse, H.H.'

Lizzie clutched my arm and said, 'Harvey, would'ya fetch some blackberries from the garden? Mr Whipple, d'ya like blackberries?'

'Mrs H.H,' said Whipple, 'I was born in a blackberry bush with a blackberry in my mouth – and quite a number of pricks in my buttocks.'

At this feeble remark Lizzie erupted with laughter and even my mother rocked back and forth in her chair, slapping her knees. I could still hear their guffaws outside as I angrily snatched fruit from the hedgerow.

On my return I found Lizzie perched at Whipple's side, my

children at his feet, and my mother in rapt silence as he regaled them with tales of trips to Paris and a poet called Baudelaire with whom he claimed to enjoy a night of mystical discovery. I hunched on a stool in the corner and watched Lizzie's bosom heaving with mirth but inches from his face.

'You must come and visit my humble home,' he said. The word *humble* enraged me for it was most likely he lived in one of those new Hackney villas with serving girls called Lucy who rang little bells when it was time for his roast duck supper. 'I absolutely must return the favour. Please come for tea – I insist upon it.'

'Oh, I should be most honoured to meet your wife, Sir,' said Lizzie. 'She must be a beautiful lady.'

Must she? I scraped at a piece of loose wattle on the wall.

'Marriage is not something that has appealed thus far,' Whipple said. 'I live very happily with a dear, dear friend. You would like him. He is a Frenchman.'

It was as clear as day. The man was a monster.

*

As August became September, an unseasonal heat gripped London, parching the land and filling the Lea Valley with a stench of rotten meat, brick dust and vinegar. A horse died on the towpath outside our gates and, in that very same week, we fished a bloated cormorant corpse from one of the beds.

At night I writhed on my sheets in the stifling heat, plagued by visions of Whipple as a poisonous raven, birds tumbling to their deaths from the sky at his passing. During the day, Lizzie pestered me for further news of our invitation to his house. I could not tell her the truth that, from the moment I woke, I was wholly preoccupied with how best to avoid Whipple. It was not easy, for he lingered perpetually on the periphery of my life, as a silhouette on a bridge, a voice drifting over a wall, or a cane swishing through the rushes. Before I departed from the filter beds each night, I would conceal myself by the gates and scan the marsh until I was certain Whipple was not on one of his deranged perambulations, but it was inevitable that I should bump into him eventually.

One evening as he crossedthe footbridge by Ashpital docks, I approached from the opposite side. By the time I realised it was he, it was too late to turn around, so I lowered my head and muttered, 'Good day, Sir' as he passed. Astonishingly, Whipple uttered not a single word of acknowledgement and shambled down the towpath without a glance back.

Four days later, noticing Whipple lingering distractedly at the beds, I decided that instead of avoiding him I would walk past with a haughty 'Good morning to you, Mr Whipple'. Yet again the scoundrel said nothing.

'Another hot day,' I added over my shoulder, peering back to gauge his response. He continued to gaze forlornly into the water, sniffing from his little vial, shoulders shaking with laughter or weeping – I could not tell, but I felt wounded, regardless. What a wretched game he played!

That night I told a tearful Lizzie that Whipple deemed us unworthy to have us in his home and that our invitation was never to be.

'He is nought but a cad,' I said, rocking her in my arms. 'You weren't to know.'

The more I thought about Whipple's wicked behaviour, the more incensed I became, resolving to confront him with my grievances. I tarried on the Lea Bridge one evening, intercepting him as he exited the public house.

'H.H!' cried Whipple.

I grabbed him by the lapels and shook him severely. 'You, Sir, are a fiend. My wife believes you think her a lowly wench unworthy of your tea.'

'Of course, yes, tea. I apologise but I have been greatly distracted of late.' He smiled. 'Problems of the heart which I have failed to solve and are to be solved on my behalf – whether I like the solution or not. Jacques has left for France and – well – I am certain now that free will is an illusion.'

'You talk gibberish!' I pushed him roughly against the barrier.

'If 'tis fisticuffs you seek, H.H, then mark you I have little left to lose.'

'You have everything in the world.'

'You do not understand – '

'I am not a fool!' I yelled.

There was a crack as the barrier gave way. Suddenly Whipple was leaning out over the Lee Navigation with I – his only saving grace – clutching him by the lapels. I heard a muted horn blast as a narrowboat approached the bridge, covered in ornate markings, bedecked with pots of tulips, mist swirling from the bow and what appeared to be white doves flapping from the aft.

'I am destined to fall,' said Whipple. 'That much is certain.'

'Then fall you must,' I said and let go of the fiend. But no sooner had I released his lapels, I realised Whipple had deviously hooked his skull-capped cane under my wife-hair necklace, bonding me to his fate.

He smiled at me. 'Where I go, you go too.'

I struggled to pull myself upright but we were inextricably linked and, besides, momentum had taken command of events. As we toppled from the bridge I expected to strike the water with a splash, but our fall was broken by the roof of the narrowboat, rolling us into the Navigation.

In the murky depths I struggled to free myself from Whipple's cane, its ivory skull leering at me as I tore at my wife-hair necklace. The hull of the narrowboat passing above us struck Whipple and latched onto his coat, hoisting us through the water at speed, like fishes on hooks. Foul water gushed into my mouth and the weed blinded my eyes as we were dragged through the Navigation until, suddenly, we were enveloped by a deep silence, falling through nothingness.

The next thing I remember is Whipple's hand gripping mine and pulling me from the water, his eyes wild. Coughing and spluttering, I felt myself hoisted by the waist and Whipple's voice whispering, 'We shall be safe down here.'

*

I awoke in a gloomy forest in the early morning light to see our sodden coats drying on a branch and Whipple's cane propped by a tree. Twigs snapped behind me and I turned to see my tormentor with a finger to his lips.

'Shhhhhh!' he said. 'I fear that unusual events have befallen us.'

I shivered with cold, my bones aching and my ears ringing with a din I could not dissipate – and yet, despite my discomfort, I welcomed these sensations, for they were signs I was alive.

'You almost killed me,' I said.

'You pushed me off a bridge,' replied Whipple. 'But 'tis of little consequence now.'

'For the first time, I must agree with you. I intend to hurry home now before I freeze to death.' I snatched my coat from the branch, slung it over my shoulder and began to walk, almost immediately confronting a sloped brick wall, crawling with vines, from which a vast iron pipe protruded.

'I told you, H.H. Most unusual.'

'My name is Harvey Hazlehurst. I thank you for pulling me from the Navigation, Mr Whipple, but I would be grateful never to hear another utterance from you until God takes my soul. Good morning to you.'

I heaved myself onto the pipe and crawled to the path, where I lay on my back momentarily to retrieve my breath. Above me, one of the stars tore through the heavens at great speed, unlike any comet I had ever seen, accompanied by a dreadful screech.

'Dear God,' I cried out.

'Gog gog gog,' said Whipple, vaulting easily onto the pipe with his long limbs, cane between his teeth. He removed the cane and said, 'God nothing. This is something else – listen!'

The sound of the star faded as it vanished from view, but other sounds of tumult persisted – a distant noise like steam escaping from vents in the earth, the parping of infernal horns, and giants hammering anvils. I presumed this phenomenon was a symptom of my water-logged ears, but Whipple could hear it too, for he grimaced as a shrill siren, fading in and out, moved from one end of the horizon to another. I was filled with unholy dread. If it were not for the chirrup of birds in the trees I would have sworn we were in Hell.

Whipple jabbed his cane at an overgrown track. 'I suggest we commence walking, to warm our blood,' he said. The track led us to a clearing where granite blocks formed a ring around a throne large enough for three or four men to sit, its mottled grey surface carved with primitive symbols.

'I have seen similar constructions,' Whipple said, 'in the South

Americas and our own Stonehenge, built for the worship of gods or for the purposes of bloody sacrifice, but not in any place along the Lea.'

Beyond the monument was a network of pipes and an iron fence, behind which I could see a weir, very much like the one I knew at Lea Bridge. There was a bridge by this weir too, illuminated by fiercely glowing oblongs on poles. A pair of bright white eyes flashed on the bridge, followed by another, and another, beams of light whirling toward us as the ground shook, sending us tumbling into the foliage for cover.

'Whatever lurks out there,' said Whipple, 'is not to be confronted until we discover more about the natives.'

'Natives? What in God's name are you talking about? How far down river do you think we were dragged?'

We hurried away from the weir, following a path parallel to the river where a stone bulwark separated us from the water below. Hooded plants like shredded umbrellas with thick, bristly stems loomed tall above this barricade. The sight of a bench, which should have been of comfort, only disconcerted me, for here it seemed more memorial to the dead than resting place for living souls.

The sky turned from dark to bright blue and the treetops reflected the first haze of sunshine. Once more we heard the scream of a star tearing the sky asunder, but on this occasion something emerged from a cloud, a steel bird, trailing steam like a locomotive. It did not itself emit the shriek – rather, the sound chased the bird across the heavens in a cosmic hunt. I cowered beside the bulwark but Whipple stood on cocked leg, rubbing his chin, apparently unperturbed.

When the bird was enveloped by cloud we proceeded towards a junction where the vegetation was less intense and it became apparent that we were atop a network of walkways, between which were deep enclosures for the cultivation of trees, or perhaps the containment of beasts we had not yet encountered. Steps led down brick slopes to these frondescent pits.

There was something extraordinarily familiar about the geometry of this junction and the burble of river behind me. With growing unease, I turned off the path and ran toward a gate, hoping my gut feeling was wrong.

'Wait.' I could hear Whipple following.

I reached the gate and turned, half-knowing what to expect, but dreading the very idea of it. My bowels turned to ice when I beheld the winch for a sluice gate, the purpose of which I knew only too well. I knew also that if I looked twenty yards further I would see the central culvert of the Middlesex Filter Beds and – lo! – there it was, revealing to me the most heinous truth.

I dropped to my knees, touched my forehead against the cold metal and sobbed, for everything and everyone I knew was dead. My dear Lizzie! My poor, poor children! My unfortunate mother! My beloved filter beds! All dead and decayed!

'I recognised this place as soon as I saw the weir,' Whipple said. 'I believe, H.H we have located ourselves on the map of "where". The question now is "when".'

I glared at Whipple, enraged. 'This is all *your* doing!'

'My dear, H.H, I completely – '

'What have you done to my mind?' Sobbing, I clawed at his legs, debasing myself most pitifully, for I could not stem the flow of my grief. 'You have drugged me! Is this what happened to Mr Graham and Mr Ackart? You fiend! Make it stop! Make it stop!'

'An opioid-induced vision of the future.' Whipple considered the thought carefully, ignoring my gnashing and wailing. 'That could explain matters. However, this is like nothing I have experienced on opiates. Hashish neither.' He extracted a small green bottle from inside his coat, wiped a wet leaf from its stopper, unplugged it and drank. 'Nor even from this fine absinthe.'

'You are the devil!!

'Better the devil you know than the devil you do not know!'

'Beast! Miscreant! Villain!'

After a goodly ten minutes exhausting my stockpile of abusive vocabulary, I could think of nothing more to throw at Whipple and lay prostrate at his feet, forsaken by my God, void of all hope. Gently, he pulled me to my feet, suppliant as a rag-doll to his will as he wiped the tears from my face with his sodden handkerchief. 'Calm yourself, my good fellow, we cannot let our emotions conquer our spirit. Day has broken. Whoever presently rules this land of the future may soon be stirring.'

Whipple decided that the best course of action was to progress calmly through the filter beds towards the back gate which led to the marsh. I knew not what to expect when we reached those gates, for if the world beyond the walls was anything like these filter beds, then it was a tomb, inert and overgrown. My suspicions were confirmed by the sight in the south westerly bed of fish with heads the size of pigs, bulbous lips sucking at the air, motionless as statues.

'What happened here, Whipple?'

Whipple sipped from his green bottle. 'Impossible to say. From this evidence it appears that without diseases to hinder him – a result of your beloved filter systems, H.H – man grew to gigantic stature. You saw that throne near the weir. Look at the size of the fish he bred to sustain him! It may be that a London populated by giants fought themselves to extinction. Look!'

He pointed his cane at the treetops, beyond which loomed an obelisk made of iron wicker, higher than a church steeple, with thick ropes looping across the filter beds to another of its kind in the distance. Fearfully we dropped behind the lip of the central culvert to observe it.

'It sees us?'

'It moves not,' said Whipple. 'But it may be aware of our presence.'

We remained concealed, watching the obelisk watching us, while the sun crawled higher into the sky, warming our clothes with its rays. Our vigil was eventually interrupted by the approaching footsteps of a negro in baggy breeches, black eyeglasses and a short silver coat, from which white string coiled from the collar into his ears.

'He is no giant,' I whispered.

As the man passed by we heard a ticking sound emanating from his ears, which seemed to determine the rhythm of his legs and the swing of his hips. We watched in amazement as he swaggered from view.

'Strange instruments are at work here,' said Whipple. 'That man is being controlled – I do believe – by an external force relating in some part to his ears. I am confident this obelisk will not interfere with us.'

With utmost caution we crept from our hiding place and moved down the ramparts, eyeing the iron wicker obelisk suspiciously. My attention was distracted by a sign beside the sand bucket which read: **How the Filter Beds Worked**. The writing beneath explained: *The filter beds were designed to clean the water from the River Lea using a filter of sand and gravel. This prevented the spread of diseases such as cholera and made the water safe to drink.* Accompanying the script were hand-drawn images of this place as I had once known it.

'Is that *you*, H.H?' said Whipple over my shoulder. In one of the pictures a man dressed rather like me stood in one of the beds shovelling sand. My knees buckled and I fell against the sign, shaking with terror.

'I am beginning to understand,' Whipple muttered. 'This place . . . 'tis a museum . . . or zoological garden. I do believe we are being observed. Much in the manner an entomologist might study insects in a moss-lined receptacle . . . and, look! I'll wager this is no coincidence . . . *someone now approaches*!'

A curly-haired man in a short black coat came towards us, a black cocker spaniel trailing behind. In his hand was a small box which he pointed at stones and leaves, as if absorbing their essence, or somehow communicating with them. I could not tell which.

'He wears no ear furniture,' Whipple remarked. 'I would hazard a guess that this man is most likely a warden!'

We stood awkwardly by the sign, Whipple with his arms akimbo, hands on hips and with my hands clasped, affecting a smile. The man spotted us but pretended he had not, for I detected a faint smirk on his face as he passed. As the spaniel sniffed my boots I resisted the urge to fling it into the bed behind me and run for the gates. The man paused as if to debate something in his mind, then he turned to us.

'Hello, I'm sorry to ask,' he said. 'I hope you don't mind. I blog about this place and I'd love to take your picture.'

Whipple replied, falteringly, 'I blog about this place too, Sir. My companion and I like nothing more than a good blog.' He patted his coat pockets. 'But alas I have no picture for you to take.'

The man laughed. 'You guys doing a shoot down here?'

'Yes,' said Whipple. 'Plenty of shooting, naturally.'

'So you don't mind, then?' I shuddered as the man shook his black box at us. 'I might tweet this if that's okay?'

I knew not what a tweet was, but this was undoubtedly the end of things for us. Whipple gently squeezed my wrist, closing his eyes peacefully, while I screwed my own shut in terror. After a dreadful, interminable silence I winked one eyelid open to see the man and his dog walking away from us.

'I cannot quite believe it!' I cried. 'We are alive – yet again! But what now?'

'Run?' suggested Whipple.

As we breathlessly followed the path towards the filter bed gates another iron bird roared across the sky, but it no longer worried us, for we had faced death and death had spurned us. Now our only recourse was to continue our progress until we were enslaved or set free by whatever creature governed this world.

To my blessed relief, the back gates were open, permitting us to run directly into a borderland of young trees, presided over by that damned iron wicker obelisk. Under the cover of foliage we stared out at Hackney Marsh, flabbergasted by a place most remarkably transformed. Gone were the rushes, sedge, reeds and sallow scrub, replaced by a uniform plain of short green grass, criss-crossed with white markings. The horizon bristled with towers, gleaming silver humps and a twisted red skeleton as tall as St Paul's Cathedral. Farther in the distance a gargantuan tower, topped with a pyramid, blinked at us.

A hopeful thought struck me. 'Could that be a church??'

'Who knows, H.H, that flashing light might be calling the populace to prayer,' said Whipple brightly. Then his brow furrowed. 'Or 'tis a demiurgic lighthouse warning folk to steer themselves away.'

Men began to run from the doors of a rusted iron building on the far side of the marsh, dressed a variety of garish shirts, their trousers truncated at the knee, revealing flesh in myriad colours and hues. White men, negros, Arabians and men of the orient mingled without dispute, kicking a ball between them.

'A game of football,' mused Whipple. 'Played between men of all races and creeds.'

'Then man here is free?'

'I have travelled the world, H.H, and if there is one thing I have learned, man is never free. This puts me in mind of those keepers of exotic animals who allow their beasts out of the cage for exercise.'

Whipple and I watched the marsh fill with men who barked coarse utterances and slapped each other's palms, clashing violently in pursuit of the ball. Presently we were surprised by a rustle of leaves behind us – a walking party consisting of two young gentlemen and a young lady approached, too late for us to hide! I held my breath as they walked past us, noting that they all wore ear furniture, although in each case the strings were attached to only one ear, allowing them to converse with each other. The girl was dressed in puffy white clothing, while the two young men were experiencing great trouble with their own apparel. For want of braces, their trouser waists languished perilously below their buttocks.

Without provocation, one of the gentlemen turned, laughing, and said, 'Yo hipsters, why don't you fuck off back to Shoreditch?' As he walked backwards, grinning, he raised his middle finger in an unusual salute.

I was unsure whether to replicate the gesture, for it was unfamiliar to me and I was aware that my response could go one of two ways. I took my chances and slowly raised my middle finger in the same manner. It was astonishing how swiftly the young man's expression curdled.

'What the fuck?' he said, covering a great deal of ground in a few swift strides and striking me across the face. I held firm, trying not to exhibit any signs of pain. 'You pussy, you want some?' He shoved me most brutally and I fell to the ground.

'Jesus Christ, leave 'em alone,' yelled the young lady. 'You's already in 'nuff shit innit.'

The man paid his good lady no heed and instead readied his foot to swing at me. Before he could crush my skull, Whipple roared, 'Stand down, Sir! We are bloggers!' and set about my attacker's head with the most extraordinary flurry of hand slaps. The young man recoiled as Whipple yelled, 'We shall tweet this, Sir, and be damned!'

The young lady shrieked with laughter, prompting our attacker to break into guffaws so uncontrollable that he could no longer stand Whipple's onslaught and returned to his companions. Hooting uproariously, they ambled across the marsh and into the woodland by the River Lea. Whipple placed a comforting hand on my shoulder but, while I was grateful for his valiant defence of my person, I could not quite bring myself to thank him.

'That young man's name was Jesus Christ,' whimpered I, tears in my eyes.

'Indeed, most strange, H.H.' replied Whipple. 'This is either a place of great devotion to God, or a place with no God at all.'

Whipple and I were faced with three wretched choices: we could sneak around the perimeter of the marsh, where we risked facing our foes in the woodland; return to the filter beds and there remain to freeze or starve to death; or walk onto the marsh in brazen view of these men and their machine rulers, thus discovering, once and for all, what our fate was to be in this world.

'For the first time in my calamitous existence, I intend to force my will upon events,' announced Whipple. 'I must sally forth and be damned. Will you accompany me?'

I was silent for a good minute, before I swallowed hard and said: 'I have always hated you, Octavius Whipple.'

Whipple's eyebrows arched. 'Truthfully? Well, that I did not know!'

'Most woefully of all, you are the closest to a friend I have in the world.' The words sickened me at their utterance. 'I shall go with you.'

The decision was made. To better integrate ourselves with the men on the marshes, we removed our coats and rolled our breeches to knee length in a loose approximation of the players' truncated apparel. However, there was little we could do to alter the style of our buckled boots. Whipple sipped the final dregs from his bottle and tossed it into the undergrowth, followed by his skull-capped cane. I removed my necklace, kissed it once, and let it fall where I stood. Thus shorn of our outer garments and personal trinkets, Whipple and I seemed suddenly very similar, shivering together at the precipice of our destinies on the edge of Hackney Marsh, brothers in time. He was unrecognisable from the outrageous dandy who arrived at the filter beds to ruin everything that day in the year of our Lord, 1861, however long ago that was. Perhaps I'd never truly known him at all.

'I suggest we place our hands over our ears as we walk,' said Whipple. 'It will conceal the fact we lack ear furniture.'

I cupped my ears. 'Like so?'

'Superlative, H.H.'

'My name, Sir, is Harvey Hazlehurst. If this be our last conversation, may you do me the honour of addressing me in the name my father bestowed upon me?'

'Very well, Harvey Hazlehurst, 'tis time to meet our fate. Remember, if anybody attempts to hinder our progress, let's inform them that we are a shooting party.'

After acknowledging each other with a terse mutual nod, we stepped out from our hiding place, hands clamped over our ears, and began our march across Hackney Marsh to much jeering and consternation.

VIII

Journey to the Rave Hole

I'm looking at a dead tree. It stands behind the railings which separate the public footpath from the Essex Filter Beds. Its trunk is wrapped in mesh wire, festooned with industrial nails. This artwork, called 'Intervention' by Jonathan O'Dea and commissioned for the cultural Olympiad, describes what architect William Mann calls the 'bastard landscape' of the Lea: a fusion of the synthetic and the natural. A laminated sign hanging from the railings explains the artwork. It tells me it's O'Dea's intention that eventually the tree trunk will rot away, leaving only a steel cast.

Wearily, I take a picture, like you're supposed to do when you see a piece of public art, like many other well-heeled middle-class types will do after me. But I'm tired of being told what to think and what to look at by the Olympic Authority, the Mayor of London, the city's planners, the advertising space brokers and centuries of cultural propaganda about what constitutes the picturesque.

Hendrix and I walk away from the tree, following the aqueduct path as it curves alongside a Victorian Waterworks Replacement depot and dips through a gulley of vegetation. I am heading towards my favourite spot in the marshland, a construction that is not art but speaks volumes about this place in a way the dead tree can't. Ahead is a concrete obelisk daubed with graffiti. A studded sludge pipe runs through it and forms arches on either side. Behind, an underpass leads beneath the Lea Bridge Road. The grilled openings of overflow pipes at the entrance are like bass bins for a steampunk soundsystem. Up above, a number 56 bus breaks cover, emblazoned with an advert for *We Will Rock You*. Faces stare down at me from its windows. They look surprised to see the underworld which appears briefly below. Then they're gone.

This is much more like it.

The obelisk was once a sluice gate controlling the flow of water through the aqueduct. You can still see the deep lateral grooves traversing both sides. What was once a doorway for water is now a portal between the city and the marshland. This underpass gives me a unique cross-section view, the branded bus advertising passing above a stark counterpoint to the graffitti in the subterranean corridors below: gargoyle faces, slogans like **BAN ALL CYCLISTS**, stencils of Tupac Shakur, geometric swirls, spot splashes and zig-zags. The names of local taggers are here: *10 Foot, Aloha, Ska, King Blue, Sense, Epidemia, Monse, Alien*. These are the invisible auteurs of the marshland. Over time their names burn themselves onto your prefrontal cortex until they are as familiar as the trees, birds and pylons.

At the obelisk I stand before the life-size image of Charlie Chaplin's iconic Tramp, painted half black, half yellow. No laminated sign interprets this piece. Chaplin once trod the boards at the Hackney Empire, so it may be a reference to this. Or it might be the work of someone who has slept in the underpass, using the Tramp icon to comment on the vagabond life. It's not always obvious what the hieroglyphics mean. This is the coded language of the dispossessed. Their scribes might not be seen, but they're there. They live where you are not. They intimate deeper, darker worlds which exist beneath the city.

Staring at Chaplin I recall a freezing winter day when I came to the graffiti underpass with Hendrix and saw a sack of clothes up ahead. As I passed by the sack reared up at me. A bearded face, eyes shut, mouth in a yawn or silent scream – I couldn't tell – pushed through the opening. As a Londoner I'm accustomed to the sight of homeless people, but this was the first time I'd seen someoneout in the marshes. This was no place to sleep. This was barely shelter at all. Only the rumble of the night bus and wailing foxes for company. I was shocked by the extremity of his exile.

'Hendrix!' I called. He was still at the entrance with his tail down, growling. I called out again. He snarled. There was nothing else for it. I had to retrieve him. As I walked back past the homeless man I raised my eyebrows and said, 'Oh, that bloody dog!'

I don't know whether I expected a chirpy rejoinder. Perhaps some part of me hoped he'd roll his eyes in sympathy. The man's face swung towards mine, his mouth a frozen 'o', his eyes deep chasms. He was too cold to enjoy the luxury of expressing emotion, and many worlds away from smiling at anything. To him I was just one of those people on the bus on Lea Bridge Road, gawping with dumb surprise at the mysterious world which has suddenly opened up beneath them.

I understood right then. This wasn't some arty edgeland heritage trail. This place was a living hub for those excluded from the city. They spoke through their own code, art and stories. They experienced extraordinary adventures beyond my comprehension. If I was going to understand this place I needed to forget the sculptures of Lea Valley's Olympiad narrative and read the naked story before my eyes.

*

I walk through the graffiti underpass and stride along the aqueduct path on a ridge of ambrosial blackberry bushes between Leyton Marsh and the paddocks of the riding centre. At the end of the ridge, the path swoops beneath two intersecting railway bridges. The white plaster walls lining this underpass encourage graffiti writers to use a linear form of conversation. A bold statement, followed by a challenger's riposte, is often followed up by a third comment:

BAN ARROGANT BASTARD CYCLISTS, THEY ARE A DANGER TO ALL
SO ARE DOGS YOU DUMB PRICK
(WHITE PUSSY)

BAN STUPID CYCLISTS
REWARD CLEVER ONES
(WITH HANGING!)

END THE FED
(I LOVE POLICE)

OPERATION GRAFFTI (sic)
SPEAD THE WORD! (sic)
(UR MOIST)

There was once graffiti on a pier of these railway bridges which

read: 'This is a pillar that holds up the train tracks. It is painted brown.' It's the sort of wry situationist commentary you don't get in the underpass beneath the Lea Bridge road.

In the run-up to the Olympics much of the graffiti here was whitewashed. Only the persistent re-appearance of ANONYMOUS: WE ARE LEGION kept the spirit alive. Within a few months of the closing ceremony, the authorities gave up. As the graffiti proliferated the politicos and local wits were drowned out in the free-for-all. Pictures of cocks, gang IDs and sex workers' phone numbers lined the walls in increasingly lurid colours. But who is to dictate what is appropriate? People feel impelled to write themselves onto the marsh for myriad reasons. The results range from coded communiqués and philosophical profundities to stupid, pointless shit. In this respect graffiti is no different to Twitter and Facebook.

What all those who write on the marshland share is a desire not to remain a passive part of their surroundings. Graffiti is not the only method for doing this. The repeated use of an area for specific activities can have the same effect. There are zones for sleeping, taking drugs and prostitution. And when it comes to dancing, the place to be is just between the railway and reservoir behind Walthamstow Marsh.

*

The Rave Hole is a secluded area of scrub and plateau of grass situated at the foot of a pylon between the reservoir fencing and the railway sidings. It's the location in the marshes where you are – or feel, at least – farthest from the city. The terrain is the fairyland of a child's imagination, undulating with steep slopes, knolls, woodland and leafy enclosures. The entrance to the Rave Hole is via a steep incline marked by two wooden posts, sometimes daubed with drawings of magic mushrooms. For a while one bore the following in blood-red paint:

D
A
N
G
E
R

I first became aware of what people did here at 11am on a blazing hot Sunday. My friend Matt and I were walking our dogs, drinking cans of lager. As we approached the Rave Hole, we came upon an apocalyptic scene. Hollow eyed refugees hobbled on the path, draped in blankets. Gaunt faces leered from the brambles. A woman lay face-down on the path, hair splayed.The grass slope was mottled orange with fag butts and packed with people. The air was filthy with coughing. Zombie hands clawed at us.

'Give us a drink mate.'

'What's in your bag? I'll buy a can!'

'Gizzasip!'

We pushed through crusties, hipsters, and gurning euro hedonists, their lips bulbous with water-retention. They flowed from an opening in the woodland, blinking in the harsh sun, as if leaving a club. An elderly bearded gentleman sat hunched by a burned out fire, arms wrapped round his knees, smiling beatifically. A Gollum creature wearing only red underpants pranced beside him, croaking gibberish.

Beneath railway bridges the ground was littered with paper wraps, licked clean of ketamine. The walls were scrawled with fresh sexual innuendo. On Walthamstow Marsh ravers mixed with family walkers. Wasters slumped unconscious on hay bales, were prodded by curious kids. Pill-heads high on the last dregs of serotonin cuddled passing dogs as hippy girls swayed to the music still playing in their minds.

'We should try and get invited to one of these,' said Matt.

'Agreed,' I said. But we both knew the truth. We didn't even know someone who might know someone who would possibly know how to get such an invite.

*

On a quiet Thursday morning Hendrix and I cut away from the footpath to explore the inner realms of the Rave Hole. We descend into a green enclosure beneath the gaze of a pylon, passing the remains of a fire, singed lager cans and a door propped against a tree. We enter woodland where an uprooted tree trunk lays on its side, fag butts and cans littering the crater it exposes. Broken concrete slabs are piled in a heap. Rubber tubing snakes from the heap and vanishes under a wire fence. One of the trees is wrapped with frayed rope, a wooden stick dangling menacingly from the end. Is this a warning sign? An occult symbol? An asphyxiation tool? Embedded in the moss on the ground is a bottle of DESPERADOS. Tequila mixed with beer. As if beer *isn't enough*. As if tequila *needed something else*. I take a photograph. There's a crash in the canopy above. Two pigeons fucking, fighting, one of the two. I find it hard to tell.

All I know is this: I am not alone.

I pick my way up the slope towards an opening in the trees, emerging in another flat green space by the railway line where a train rattles by. Scorched discs show where campfires have been.

I push through a corridor of foliage into a sheltered area at the pylon's foot. Many of the branches are stripped of bark. The floor is littered with empty cans of Polish lager

Coke bottles   polystyrene plates

                                        plastic bags

                The Mirror

a sock, soiled   fragments of cardboard box

        a whittled stick

In one corner the bushes drip with streamers of tissue. The odour of bodily fluids hangs in the air. I take my pictures quickly and leave.

There is no path or mud-track through the scrub towards the reservoir, but I notice the grass has been recently trodden and follow the trail along the fence of the reservoir, crested with spikes, skeletal towers looming beyond. The railway angles ever closer to the reservoir, narrowing the scrub into a wedge. As I take photos I hear deep voices. A foreign language, but familiar. Arabic, perhaps, I'm not sure. I wonder if there are workers on the rails. Hendrix and I come upon a low canopy of trees, which forms an alcove where a man hangs by his hands from a branch, trousers down, boxer shorts round his ankles. Another man is crouched before him. Two others sit on a felled tree-trunk, as if waiting for the dentist.

I freeze, camera poised in front of me. The man on the branch turns his head. The man at his crotch dives for cover. Time stops.

We stare at each other, trapped by mutual embarrassment. It's hard to know what to say to a semi-naked man hanging from a tree at the best of times. The man on the ground is curled into a ball, arms over his head, like a five year-old's hedgehog impersonation. Hendrix is oblivious, weaving through the grass towards the men. I realise I have to break the deadlock before he reaches them. My dog is what you would describe as *a licker*.

'Hendrix!' I yell. A spiral of wood pigeons and crows flap into the air. Time cracks open. A startled Hendrix races back towards me and I walk from the scene as quickly as I can without breaking into a run. I rush through the Rave Hole with the ozone whiff of semen, piss and blood chasing me up the slope to the path. Behind me in the Rave Hole there are four men, maybe more, wondering whether I've caught them on film.

*

A steep grassy ridge overlooks the path at the entrance to the Rave Hole. On a bench at the top you can take in the view of Clapton rising into Stamford Hill on the far side of the river. This is a popular drinking spot. A dip in the earth beside the bench is littered with crushed cans and fag butts. The concave slope of the ridge forms an amphitheatre, turning whoever sits at its crest into a Roman Emperor with powers of judgment over those passing below.

One afternoon, Hendrix and I walked past the Rave Hole into view of the ridge. A group at the top turned their heads in unison, as if they had been awaiting me. On the bench a middle-aged man in a 1970s football manager's coat, clinging to the collars of two lurchers, looked every bit the geezer. Beside him sat a lad in a crumpled suit and another in a Nike T-shirt, both supping from cans of cider. A woman in a tracksuit stood by them, smoking. They stared intently as I ambled past. I couldn't be certain, but the guy in the T-Shirts seemed to be barking at me.

'Mate – that a poodle?' the girl yelled.

'Don't be stupid, no it aint,' the geezer said to her.

'Sorry?' I said.

'I'm telling yer,' she jabbed her fag at him, 'it's a poodle.'

'No way.'

'I'll swear on my life that's a poodle.'

'Do what you like, girl, it ain't one.'

'Oi!' she called to me again, 'what kind of dog is that?'

'It's a cocker spaniel,' I replied. Her face fell.

'Ha!' spat the geezer. The boy in the suit snorted.

'It aint a poodle?'

'No,' I said.

'I thought it was a poodle, I coulda swore it was a poodle.'

'It's obviously a cocker spaniel,' said the geezer.

'It looks like a poodle innit.'

'But it aint a poodle.'

'Why does it look so much like a poodle?' she asked me. 'Is it a cross . . . I mean . . . you know, a . . . oh, whatcha call it . . . a *poodle doodle*?'

'LABRA-FACKIN'-DOODLE,' cried the geezer.

'Yeah, that's it.'

'It's a cocker spaniel,' I confirmed.

'Don't worry 'bout her,' the geezer laughed, 'she don't know her dog breeds from her arsehole. Just ask her boyfriend. He'll tell you all about it.'

He nodded towards the man with the cider.

'Woof woof,' barked the boyfriend.

It was time to go.

This was a rare encounter with the marshes' drinkers. They are as elusive as badgers but signs of their boozing lie all around. Polish lager tins bob among the reeds. The railway sidings glisten with cans. Leafy nooks are scattered with vodka bottles, soggy newspapers and meringues of tissue. Desire paths hewn by human feet cut across the scrub into enclosures where boozing can commence in peace.

The marshland offers drinkers refuge from an increasingly privatised city. There's no family to disappoint. No police to move them on. No doctor telling them what to do. No advertising hoardings telling them what they should be like and what they should want. They are one of multiple subcultures thriving beyond the reach of mainstream society. Men who aren't permitted by their culture to have sex with other men can fulfil their desires. Ravers who aren't permitted to play loud music or gather in public places gather here to play loud music. Teenagers who aren't allowed to do anything at all can smoke, drink, share tales, experiment with drugs and sex. Addicts can self-medicate in peace.

Some days, when life at home has been particularly screamy with kids these alcoholic fragments are to me like internet pop-up ads where goggle-eyed demons shriek *Drink this! Drink this! Drink this! Drink this!* I want to crawl into the bushes on all fours and stick my tongue down the neck of a bootleg vodka bottle, just to get a dab of that sweet potato nectar. I want to gamble with that quarter-full Lucozade bottle at my feet. Yes it might be urine, but might as easily be a Lucozade with mixer, laced with the latest designer drug – Roflcopter, Meow-Meow or whatever it is the kids use to smelt their spinal cords these days. I'm tantalised by two cans of Super T and Special Bew side-by-side, titans of the strong lager market slugging it out in the marshland.

Days like these my soul fills with a yearning to sit beneath a pylon and guzzle wine until the sky turns red, nurse a bottle of whisky beneath the moon, and wait for my fellow drinkers to emerge from the darkness to tell wild stories of a world on the edge. I imagine waking up alone under a cool sun, fields stretching out in every direction, London a hazy mirage in the distance. A kestrel will swoop down from a pylon to ask me, in the voice of Vincent Price, 'Good morning, sir, what is it you would like to do today?' I will pick up the bottle, swish around the contents and say with a yawn: 'I think I would like to sit here.'

IX

Temples of the Neo Gods

Look west from Walthamstow Marsh and you see a spire poking from the humped ridge of Upper Clapton. It has an eerie quality, switching from jet black to brown to silver grey, depending on the light, constantly pricking the periphery of your vision, a thorn in your eyeball. You might consider this church to be a relic of prudish Victorian London, where locals dressed in their finery once mumbled their devotion to God on cold Sunday mornings. You'd be wrong. This building was constructed by the messianic leader of a West Country sex-cult.

The Church of the Ark of the Covenant, known today as the Church of the Good Shepherd, was built in 1892 by the Agapemone ('Abode of Love') cult, whose leader, Henry James Prince, had come from Somerset to establish a wing of his spiritual community in London. Prince was a charismatic evangelist who, as a young preacher in the early 19th Century, received divine instruction from the Holy Ghost. These divine missives gradually convinced him that he was the Messiah, and immortal. He told his followers that the day of judgement was nigh and they should offer him their worldly possessions. In 1846 Prince used this money to purchase a plot of land in the village of Spaxton, Somerset, where he built a country house with outhouses, stables, gardens, workers' cottages, ringed by a high wall.

Prince began an aggressive recruitment drive, marrying off male cult members to wealthy Somerset spinsters and drawing those women into the Spaxton community, whether they liked it or not. Once inside the walls, the new Agapemonites were cut off from friends and family. They lived in chastity and worked the gardens while Prince dwelled in his eighteen bedroom house, enjoying fine wines and unlimited sex with his most attractive followers, who were to become known as his 'soul brides'.

The more he gorged on this earthly bounty, the more certain Henry James Prince became of his infallibility as the son of God. To test this presumption, he invited his followers to the chapel to witness a ceremony called The Great Manifestation. As his congregation sang to the strains of a pounding church organ, he raped Zoe Patterson, a sixteen-year-old virgin, on the altar. Some disenchanted followers fled, but a hardcore remainder believed Prince's theory that the now pregnant Patterson was carrying Satan's spawn, not his own.

In the ensuring outrage, the community closed itself off from the outside world. Journalists took up residence at The Lamb, a pub outside the Agapemonite walls, and wrote hysterically lurid stories about what supposedly went on behind those walls. A steady drip-feed of sex scandals, brainwashing accusations and kidnapping capers kept Victorian Britain titillated for another thirty years.

By 1892, Prince was 85 years old and his most ardent devotees were by now convinced of his immortality. After decades hidden behind his Spaxton walls he emerged with new ambitions and

enough money to construct a 155 foot tall gothic church in Upper Clapton. A bull and a lion flanked the doorway, above which an inscription read:

LOVE IN JUDGEMENT AND JUDGEMENT UNTO VICTORY.

The building was a glorious consolidation of his divine right. Preachers queued up to speak at the church. Henry James Prince was a Messiah at the very top of his game.

When he died suddenly in 1899, it came as quite a surprise.

His panicked disciples hurriedly buried him – upright, allegedly – in an unmarked grave in the Spaxton community garden, hoping to facilitate a speedy resurrection. When nothing happened, there was another exodus. Those who remained decided it was a good idea to replace their dead Messiah with a new one.

The perks of the job being well-known, it wasn't hard to find a successor. The Revered John Hugh Smyth-Pigott was a regular preacher at the Church of the Ark of the Covenant. He gladly accepted the role, despite a jeering crowd at his inauguration and the need for local police escort to help him exit the church. Switching his time between Spaxton and Clapton, Smyth-Pigott tucked into his diet of spiritual brides with an even greater gusto than Prince. To further consolidate his position, he also declared himself immortal, a proper immortal this time, rather than a failed immortal like Prince. He wasn't some flimsy conduit for the Holy Spirit or a measly son of God. His divinity went all the way to the top of the trinity.

On 7th September 1902 his congregation was surprised to find that the communion table had been removed. In its place was a chair in which the Reverend Smyth-Pigott sat, pointing to the ceiling. He explained that God was no longer above them, but – now he pointed at himself – here in this room. As cries of disbelief went up, Smyth Pigott told them that he had it on good authority

– namely, his own – that God's son would appear in the Church of the Ark of the Covenant. Christ was coming to Clapton.

But this was London, not Somerset. Riots broke out. The police tried to keep an angry mob from tearing Smyth-Pigott to pieces. His sceptical followers demanded that he prove his divinity by walking across Clapton Pond. Smyth-Pigott declined the offer and fled to Spaxton, a place where a man could run a divine sex-cult in relative peace. He lived out his days servicing soul brides and shepherding a dwindling flock until his death in 1927.

Today the Church of the Ark of the Covenant is known as the Church of the Good Shepherd. From the marsh it looks small on a cluttered horizon, but it's impossible to ignore. Like many landmarks on the London skyline it represents a persistent human desire to create utopias in which we assume control over a chaotic world, and the role of architecture as an instrument of that control.

The spire of the Church of the Ark of the Covenant was not built to reach up towards God. It was a lightning rod conducting heavenly powers down to earth so that Smyth-Pigott and Prince could rule others in a pleasure garden of their own making.

*

A few miles south an isolated pink 1960s tower block broods on the edge of Hackney Marsh. The melancholy gaze of its windows follows you like the eyes on a renaissance portrait as you cross the football pitches. It used to be called Sudbury Court until the 1990s when it was refurbished, painted pink and renamed 'Landmark Heights'. In 2005 it was chosen as the setting for *Bullet Boy*, directed by Saul Dibb. The protagonist, Ricky lives with his brother, Curtis and mother in the upper floors, with much of the action shot around Hackney Marsh.

If you type 'Landmark Heights' into Google Maps and zoom in close, you'll see this building is marked: 'The Office of Deputy Prime Minister of the Kingdom of God'. For this is the residence of Mr Serge Grishenkoff Jr., the deputy Prime Minister of the Kingdom of God – and possibly also its Prime Minister, Mr Serge Grishenkoff Sr. In the upper reaches of this tower block in Clapton Park, he has established the government office of an independent world state outside the jurisdiction of the United Kingdom, whose borders are dictated by race and religion. The government's website lays out a manifesto:

'Registration of all Nationals, Nations and Corporations as Subjects of the Kingdom of God, provided that all Subjects of Europe (save Albania and Malta), Russia, Canada, US, Australia, and New Zealand are Japhetic (White) Christian, and all others are Hamito-Semitic (Colored) Christian, Muslim, or other Subjects, and that all Nationals enjoy freedom of movement, residence, employment, possession, marriage, and adoption, and all Subjects enjoy freedom of their affairs, only in Nations of their Race and Religion, subject to Repatriation.'

In this harmoniously repatriated world, all races have a degree of entitlement to God's Kingdom except the Jews who, declares Grishenkoff, are a cabal of conspirators intent on establishing a new world order through control of the banks, governments and the media. He describes it as a 'rebellion disguised as religion'. The perpetrators of this rebellion are to be 'executed' and their property restored to the Kingdom. Girshenkoff's logic is that he is not anti-semitic, for the Jews are not semites but a distinct minority group of criminals and perverts who have brainwashed humanity with 'the holocaust, dinosaurs and other scams'.

The Kingdom of God has multiple accounts on most social

media platforms including MySpace, Facebook and Linked In. Its primary Twitter account is prolific, endlessly repeating the same slogans and accusations. They range from grand declarations like 'The Kingdom of God is the world state without any wars, and if you are not a Jew or a pervert you can be its Subject', to specific claims like: 'Allowing the jews to exclusively teach us is committing an academic suicide. Metropolitan and Westminster Universities destroyed my theses.'

It's easy to mock the horny Victorian parson building his hilltop church and the 21st Century racist ruling his internet micronation from a Hackney tower-block. But the arc of London's landmarks, as seen from the marshes is a series of ideologies exposed through architecture.

To the south of the marsh rises the Olympic Park, built for a corporate-branded spectacle showcasing our conquering of time and gravity. The Westfield shopping centre is a permanently anchored retail cruise liner. Anish Kapoor's hunchbacked helter skelter prowls Stratford like a colonial overlord. An illuminati eye winks from a pyramid atop Canary Wharf, a cluster of skyscrapers built during the `80s banking boom for the High Priests of finance, who believed in the liberation of society through the free flow of capital. Their power was such that they could profit from the movement of money from commodity to commodity. Up or down, it didn't matter. Crashes became profit opportunities. Bubbles became get rich quick schemes. The money markets became unsustainable pyramids demanding ever more input from the workers at the bottom. Banks became the house, and we became the gamblers. Great casinos rose into the sky. From Canary Wharf to the Gherkin and Heron Towers at the gates of the City, their edifices shimmer like mirages. Thrusting higher than them all is The Shard, an irregularly stepped pyramid which echoes Bruegel's *Tower of Babel*, depicting that legendary attempt to create a utopia on earth.

These are the temples of the neo-gods. We are told these keep us in fuel, schools and houses and that their collapse will be the end of us. That there is no alternative. But they are only another turn in the cycle of the city's history. Towers rise, towers fall, towers rise again. Many of these temples to money and speculation are built on sites which were once home to docks, factories and fisheries – architecture propelled by the ideals of Empire.

In South Millfields the red brick elevation of a ruined coal-fired power station looms over the Lee Navigation. Once it gobbled fossil fuels and spewed out carbon dioxide. Today it shelters the Millfields recycling plant beneath its walls. In the yard a parade of black and green bins is assembled in rows to await execution in a military green prefab where machine jaws grind. Next door is the Millfields Electricity Depot, a corrugated block festooned with stalactites of electrical coil and a network of silver pipes like the exposed engine of a nuclear submarine. Electricity is carried here by godlike pylons which stride through the Lea Valley, blasting energy to the televisions, kettles, X-Boxes, computers, power tools, halogen weed-cultivation lamps, mixing desks and bedside vibrators of the city. One day these pylons, which brought us our electric nirvana, will be gone too, replaced with underground cables.

This is the way of the city. London is a palimpsest. Industrial sites overlay agricultural ones. Sites of commerce replace those of industry. Private regency gardens become public parks. Public spaces become privatised. Abandoned factories, power plants and sewerage systems are transformed into museums, galleries and recreation zones. Schools become mezzanine apartment blocks. High street bank branches become betting shops. Pubs become flats. Churches become pubs. Everything is overwritten, eventually. There is no final draft of London. In the marshland you can stand upon the ruin of old water filter schemes, look out and see the cranes hoisting the new schemes into place: temples for sports and leisure, international property development and high finance. Seen from this wide green hole in London, the skyline is a parade of ruins, future and past, each saying something about humankind's desire to engineer the world.

X

The Ghost Factory

Overlooking the Lee Navigation by the Homerton Road on the corner of Hackney Marsh are three apartment blocks known as Matchmaker Wharf. Its architecture traces the outline of a factory which was once the operation centre of Lesney Industries Ltd, manufacturer of the iconic Matchbox toy cars, founded by Leslie & Rodney Smith in 1947 and eventually closed in 1982.

The factory was still standing in 2008 when I came to the marshland. At first I didn't realise it was abandoned. A barge bobbed expectantly against the wharf. A hook in the loading bay seemed to swing gently. On second glance, the hook was still. A face appeared in a window, a pair of spectacles glinting, but on closer inspection it was only sunshine glancing off the shards of a smashed window pane. What seemed at first to be life was only light dancing on decay.

Many windows were intact, some propped open to let the air in, freezing in time a musty day in the office in 1982. Someone sick of the smell of Embassy No.1s and over-heating fax machines. Bill in accounts had sweat circles under his arms and stank out the place in summer. In winter he always moaned about the cold. Debbie the receptionist couldn't stand him. At least that's what she told her colleagues in the canteen every day. Oh, how they laughed when she was caught with Bill's hand up her skirt at the Christmas party, the last one before the factory closed. Bill and Debbie. Who would have thought it? He was a dirty bastard that Bill.

I fell for the factory immediately. The blue lettering of the 'Lesney' sign reminded me of factories of my childhood. In the `80s my dad was a personnel manager for an alloy factory in Glossop, Derbyshire, a town in the foothills of the Pennines. His office was a similar building which I'd visit at lunchtime during the school holidays to go fell-running with him and his workmates. I remember scruffy, featureless cubes, filled with paper and files, where typewriters clattered, phone bells trilled and the corridor carpets charged you with electricity as you scuffed along. The changing rooms in the basement smelled of sweat and cologne. For me it was a domain of kings. This was where adults of the world did their work, making things. And when they weren't making things they were running through the hills like moustachioed huntsmen in Ron Hill tracksuits.

Standing there in 2008 I was naive to imagine that Lesney was still functioning. We don't make things these days, certainly not toy cars, just talk to my phantom friend Bill from accounts.

'I blame Thatcher,' he says bitterly. 'That free market crap. Now we've lost it all.' His face is drawn. There's a picture of Debbie in a heart-shaped frame on his desk. He works at an old people's home now. Old people are bigger business than die-cast model cars. It's one of the last boom markets. Besides, what else could he do after Lesney? Fly high in the City? Get a job in the media? Run a sex shop in Soho? No, I prefer to think of Bill as forever roaming the Lesney factory, giving it the big 'I am' to the office girls. Not only Bill but generations of workers for whom this austere block of brick was the hub of daily life.

In 2010 the bulldozers came to tear down the toy factory. Each day another chunk of wall was torn away. Slowly they exposed the internal organs of Lesney. Tongues of carpet flapped in the breeze. Sticks of fluorescent lighting swung from wires. A bleak blossom of insulation foam fluttered to earth. I saw bell-bottomed ghosts with sideburns and mullets striding through these corridors in the air, unaware that the ground beneath their feet was crumbling. That June 1973 deadline still needed to be hit, and to hell with what was happening in June 2010. The future was a another universe.

After a month of demolition only a ruined turret of the factory's far corner remained. Rubble filled the loading bay. The blue 'Lesney Industries Ltd' sign was almost gone, a final 'u' hanging on for dear life. Then that fell too. Diggers crawled over a mound of stones, beetles on a corpse. Men in hard hats held charts and pointed authoritatively at parts of the ground. A few weeks later they started building Matchmaker Wharf.

I watched the new edifices grow, day by day. Slowly the apartments began to fill the shape of the former factory. As a nod to the past, the architects kept the loading bay beneath the social housing block of the development. In the courtyard between the two private towers they installed a statue of a loop-the-loop track with two toy cars on it. To document the resurrection I photographed the apartments at each stage of their development. But every time I looked for long enough I could still see the factory and those old toymakers walking in the sky.

XI

Biomass

On their first night in Matchmaker Wharf they are woken by a diabolical screech. It rises through the floor, curls its fingers round their spinal cords, and yanks down hard, jerking them upright on their mattress. A clamour of hammers shakes the walls and the room fills with a sulphuric stink. Her almond eyes are wide and terrified.

'What's happening? Go and see!'

He staggers naked through the empty flat, tripping over the discarded champagne bottles, a condom wrapper stuck to his heel. The cacophony comes from all sides, the hammering now joined by the sound of something heavy swinging on a rusty hinge, and the rhythmic grating of sandpaper on bone. *What the fuck is that?* He grabs his iPhone. No reception in this bloody place. A £285,000 flat with marsh views and access to the Olympic Park and no reception, except on the balcony. Tutting, he staggers to the French doors, waggling his phone in the air.

Outside he's shocked by the sudden silence. Hackney Marsh is a deep blackness crested with a halo of light from the North

Circular. There's something on the towpath below, by the steps of the Homerton Road Bridge. Two hot coals glow in a seething mass of darkness which expands and shrinks like a slowly beating heart. At first he thinks it's an animal of some kind, a bear maybe. Ridiculous. He shakes the sleep from his eyes and stares harder. It's a human figure – a man, though he's not sure. All he knows that, whatever it is, it's looking up at him, and it's angry.

When he returns to the room she's sitting with the sheet pulled up to her neck. He slips in beside her and cradles her close. Her skin is cold. He doesn't mention the figure on the towpath. Neither does she admit to him that she shivers not with fear, but with guilt.

Last night she lay on her back while he writhed on top of her and thought of several far more successful men who weren't him.

The awful noise, she worries, it's an omen. This whole moving-in together thing was a mistake.

*

The next morning there's a knock at the door. With a pounding headache he answers it to a middle-aged man wearing a white shirt and tie beneath an olive cardigan, reeking of cigarettes. Forests of hair sprout from his nostrils. He clutches a plant pot. A single stem with a withered leaf dangles over the rim.

'I'm Mr Fulcher. You can call me Fulcher.' He shakes his hand vigorously. 'So you're the new one then? The new boy? Here.' He thrusts the pot into his hands. 'It should spruce up nice 'n' proper if you stick it by the window.'

'Hello, sorry, I'm not feeling very well. This is very kind but . . .'

Fulcher leans in close, winking conspiratorially, and whispers, 'So . . . how is she getting along?'

'How's who?'

'Her indoors. Very tasty, even for a darkie.'

'I don't follow.'

'Oh right, fair do's. That's kosher,' says Fulcher. 'Mum's the word. We're all very discreet here. Just thought I'd let you know. There's a hiccup with the biomass boiler in the basement. Water pressure's on the wonk. An engineer's coming to fix the valve settings. Your back-up boiler will need looking at.'

He has no idea what a biomass boiler is, but he says, 'Well that might explain the noise.'

'Noise?' Fulcher's noise wrinkles.

'You didn't hear it? Last night?'

'Nah, slept like a baby. Look, gotta rush. Busy busy. You just be here for the engineer. Monday afternoon between twelve and five. Tatty bye!'

When he closes the door, she's standing in the hallway behind him. 'What does he mean by *darkie*?'

'You're beautiful when you're angry. Look, he bought us a dead plant. What more could you want?'

She shrugs away his touch, shaking her head. This is what her father doesn't like about him. *He doesn't take life seriously enough. He's weak. He won't defend you.* Then again, her father is a patriarch who, despite her success as a lawyer, sees her as nothing more than an overpaid secretary to the men who run the City. Perhaps that's the reason she's combined mortgage deposits with a heavy drinking salesman she's been seeing only a year. Revenge. But she's too tired to think about it. It's a blissfully quiet morning after last night's disturbance. They've got two weeks off to decorate the flat. She's got some great colour schemes in mind, right out of *Elle Decoration*, which will really improve the place. If it all goes pear-shaped they can flip the property for a fat profit in a year's time and walk away from each other, cash rich.

It'll be fine. They may as well go back to bed.

*

They spend the afternoon at B&Q, blearily watching paint judder in the mixing machines. They pop across the car park to ASDA (*'ASDA?'* she sneers) where they pick up some stationery, including a note-book to write the snagging list for the property's management company, Randal & Ricks. A surprising amount needs fixing. Broken doorstop. Faulty hob. Loose panel on the wardrobe in the bedroom. Stain on the carpet in the spare room. Water dribbles from the bathroom taps. He decides a calendar will help them stay organised. The only one left has photos of cats in yoga poses. He gets it anyway.

To her dismay, they stop at a second-hand furniture store where he insists on buying an old office desk, a couple of chairs and a landline phone. 'I'm not standing on the balcony every time I want to call someone or use the internet,' he explains, noting her distaste. 'We'll get rid of it when we bring our own stuff in from storage.'

When they return home, Fulcher is standing by their open front door, tapping his watch. 'What time you call this?' he says. 'Never mind, I've let 'em in.'

Two men in white overalls dither by their boiler cupboard. As they enter, the men nod tersely.

'You said Monday,' he says to Fulcher, confused.

'It is Monday,' says Fulcher.

'But it can't be.'

She checks her phone. Shows it to him, grimacing. Fulcher is right. It is Monday. She feels terrible suddenly, as if her neck glands are filling with battery acid. She goes into the bathroom, slams the door, and begins heaving into the toilet bowl.

'Dontcha worry 'bout her.' Fulcher is standing inside their hallway, sipping tea from a mug with Princess Diana's face on it. 'She'll soon get used to the pace of things.'

*

What the hell's wrong with her? For a moment, as he pushes the new desk into the corner of the living room and plugs in the phone, he wonders if she's pregnant, but she can't be, they're so careful, mainly on her part, murmuring about her career even in the thick of lust, if you can call it that. The line is dead, of course, like everything else round here. Nothing works. He'll need to arrange a hook-up. Get them connected. Then he can start making some calls about this infernal noise problem.

He unwraps the new calendar and marks the day with a cross. It's less than twenty-four hours since they got the keys to the apartment on a Saturday afternoon but now it's Monday. A day is missing. It doesn't make sense. He tears a page from the notebook, and writes the date and time at the top of it. He decides to note down every passing hour and detail what's occurred. Just to keep track. He pins the calendar on the wall and blu-tacs the piece of paper next to it.

'Very nice.' Fulcher is standing so close behind he can hear air straining through his nose hair.

'What are you doing in here?'

'Men have gone. Pressure is restored.' Fulcher points at the calendar. 'You seem busy.'

'I'm getting organised.'

'Good,' says Fulcher. 'You'll do well here. I'll check back on you tomorrow. Tatty bye.'

The front door clicks shut. He can hear Fulcher in the corridor, fumbling with his keys. Why would a single middle-aged man need such a large bunch? What does Fulcher actually do? He shuts his eyes, overwhelmed with tiredness.

When he opens them again, it is dark. The back of the chair is sore against his shoulders. There's a sound of muffled explosions on the marsh, like bombs exploding on soft earth. He wanders to the French doors and steps outside. Something catches his eye, down by the bridge. It's that figure again, in the same spot, watching.

There's a flash of white – a hand, pointing at him. He feels the figure's rage pulsing the air, rattling the windows. Something unseen whistles through the sky. An explosion hits the marsh and shakes the balcony so hard he has to grip the barrier. The air-vents of Matchmaker Wharf clang open, unleashing a howl from the depths of the building.

He hears her cry out. He stumbles to the bedroom and finds her coiled on the mattress with the pillows wrapped around her head, sobbing.

'I'm sorry,' he says, getting in beside her, rocking back and forth to the sound of the creaky hinge. 'This is all my fault.' He doesn't know what he means by that. The words just fall out, like someone else has spoken them.

*

After days languishing on the mattress, sweating and semi-conscious, it all begins to make sense to her. All these jitters about him, and the vomiting. It was probably all down to stress. It's usual for City professionals to get ill when they take a holiday off work. Her colleagues are always moaning about this phenomenon. It's definitely a thing. She's not taken a long break in years and perhaps that's the problem. She's never been one for relaxing, doing nothing. She gets bored easily – of everything, sex, men, domesticity. That's all it is. The sooner they get going on their job list the better. It's up to her to make the effort. She dresses herself in that figure-hugging business suit he finds sexy, carefully applies her makeup and goes to see what's happening.

He's been busy. Really busy. The living room floor is a mess of scrunched paper. A plastic portable radio in the corner of the room is playing an old Leo Sayer hit, the one about dancing. He adjusts his tie, coughing nervously, beckons her in and sits her down at the desk, strewn with stationary and scribbled notes

With a serious frown he explains to her, slowly, that she should not panic, but the truth of the matter is, it is still Monday, the same Monday the men came to check the boiler. He shows her the date on his iPhone.

'It can't be!'

'I've been keeping track. Look.' Post-it notes dotted along the wall detail the number of tasks carried out in each hour of the day and the number of 'sleeps' he has experienced within a calendar day. Each 'sleep' is allocated a Roman numeral followed by the date and a sun or moon symbol. A piece of A4 headed 'KEY NOTES!!!' is Sellotaped to the desk.

'I've woken up and gone to sleep five times,' he says. 'It has got dark and then light again six times. Nothing matches up. But time is passing. Look at my moustache.' She smiles at the sight of the black bush sprouting on his lip. She's always hated moustaches, but for some reason this one excites her. It reminds her of someone, but she can't remember who. Certainly not him. And that's good. It's really good.

'Now you're back in action, I need you to organise the snagging list,' he explains with calm authority. 'I will try to get some answers about the noise. It must be this biomass boiler. The pipes or something.'

She nods. It's okay that he's taking charge for once. She likes the way he rubs his new moustache when he's concentrating. She doesn't even mind that he's started smoking. It gives him a manly, musky odour. With rising excitement, she hopes he notices that the three top buttons of her blouse are undone.

'What do I do then?' She looks at the calendar. May's picture is of a cat doing a leg stretch. The date boxes are thick with markings. Above the calendar is a page torn from *The Sun*. A large-breasted girl is saying, 'Performance-enhancing drugs have no place in Britain's Summer of Sport.'

He stubs out a John Player Special and slides the note-pad towards her. 'Timetable the workmen coming from Randal & Ricks. Use the snagging list to guide you.'

Orders given, he goes to the balcony to look for their stalker. A cyclist swerves to avoid a man walking a black cocker spaniel. An elderly couple stroll over the bridge. A fisherman packs away his bait. None of these people match the profile of the figure he sees on the towpath every night. All the same, he feels he's being watched. The tree tops shake and two crows flap out over Hackney Marsh. *What lurks in the undergrowth? What's out there?*

When he comes back in, she looks up with a half-smile. He's struck by the curve of her leg, hint of bra strap on her shoulder and the way she taps her fingernail on her front teeth.

The minx.

She gasps when he stops to caress her shoulder. Her pen drops. He stoops and they kiss. Her mouth is surprisingly hot and salty, like that very first time. He lifts her, pushes her hard against the desk, knocking the ashtray onto the floor. She groans. Arches her

back. Lifts her skirt. Wraps her legs around him.

There's a knock at the door.

'Fulcher!' he gasps.

They hurriedly straighten themselves out. She yanks down her skirt, flushing with embarrassment. He paces the room, red faced and puffing, willing his erection to disappear. He urges her to go to the door. Tell Fulcher he's out or something. She fearfully shakes her head.

'Christ . . . ' He walks slowly through the hallway, tucking in his shirt. When he peers through the peephole he sees a giant bloodshot eye staring back at him. He opens the door.

'How's my favourite new boy?' says Fulcher, unsmiling.

'Good afternoon.'

'It's the morning.'

'Is it?'

'Last time I checked. Hope you're behaving in there?'

'We were working on our schedules.'

'I'd like to think so,' says Fulcher. 'Because I got you this.' He holds out a wall clock horizontally as if it's a birthday cake. 'Newgate. Classic. Got one in my office. Can't go wrong with Newgate.'

'It's very kind of you.'

'Oh, no bother. It's what I'm here for.' Fulcher lowers his voice. 'Talking of which, if you fancy a boys-only break, I could show you round? Reckon she's got plenty to be getting on with, eh?'

He senses her lingering in the doorway of the living room. She dislikes Fulcher, he doesn't blame her for that. But he's the man at the top and they can't go on, night after night, suffering their cacophonous torment. There are questions about the building he needs to ask. Fulcher is the man to answer them. He steps out and closes the door behind him.

'I'd like to see this biomass boiler,' he says.

*

In the lift Fulcher tells him that biomass boilers work in the same way as regular gas central heating boilers, except they run on organic matter. 'The gubbins that usually ends up in landfill,' he explains. 'Mashed into chips and chucked into the boiler. But they've gone a bit experimental down here.'

The lift doors open in a basement. Steps lead down into a dark room as cold as a mine shaft. Fulcher buttons his cardigan to the top and ushers him towards a set of locked swing doors. A sign says STAFF ONLY. Through the windows he can see a white box with silver flumes rising into the ceiling. The boiler gasps and clicks. It reminds him of a crisp December day at a crematorium in Bristol. His mum's funeral. That slick mechanical whirr, a whisper of fire.

'See them,' Fulcher directs his gaze to three black pipes protruding from the side of the boiler and curving into the cement floor. 'Them's the experimental bit.'

'They're pipes.'

'Yeah, but it's what goes *through* the pipes. Most getups like this have a big vat for wood pellets and the like. Something to feed the boiler.'

'So what feeds this one?'

'This is the site of the old toy factory. You know that, right? Like most of them industrial plots they're building the Olympics on, it's contaminated with all sorts. Hackney Marsh too. You don't want to know what's under them football pitches. During the Blitz they dumped rubble there. Smashed up houses. Shrapnel. Body parts. You name it.'

'Those pipes come from under the marsh?' He feels queasy suddenly. A small glass portal on the left panel pulses red and green. An artery in his neck starts to thump in time to it. He claws at his collar.

'Yeah, a lotta memories out there,' sighs Fulcher. 'A lotta memories.'

*

Now that there's an office clock on the wall there's no need to check the time on their mobiles. After a while the screens go dark. They don't bother to recharge. The thought of text messages and missed calls fills them with dread. They've had too little sleep. Explosions, rumbles and creaking pervade every waking night. During the day the walls vibrate. They're so accustomed to it they hum along as they pass each other in the hallway. Besides, they have too many projects on the go to worry about texts.

Busybusybusy.

There's the calendar project. The noise-monitoring project. The scheduling of decoration and repairs. Letters of complaint to write to Randal & Ricks. Letters to Telford homes requesting floor plans. Letters to GeoBiomass, manufacturers of the biomass boiler. He dictates while she uses the laptop as a glorified typewriter. Fulcher comes in regularly to check their progress and offer pointers. She doesn't like the way the men leave the room to talk in private but she's happy their efforts are paying off. Boys will be boys and all that.

The handymen arrive after what could be five or six days to work through the snagging list, although they insist it's Monday, even though their post-it notes show that many weeks have passed. The flat becomes a hive of industry as the men go to work. He directs the operations with a cocky energy she finds irresistible. She makes tea for everyone and pretends to get cross about the cigarette smell.

'We really must open a window in here,' she smiles, wafting her hand through a brown cloud of John Player Special smoke.

On the afternoon their landline telephone is finally connected they wait until the workers leave at five and celebrate by dialling the speaking clock. He reads out the time while she totters on a chair in her heels adjusting the Newgate wall clock. Grinning, he runs a hand up her thigh.

'Not here!' she gasps, laughing. 'Not yet.'

'Let's celebrate properly. When was the last time we had a drink?'

He rushes to the mini-market to buy wine. On his return he spots Fulcher in the foyer. He is gesticulating wildly at the concierge, but the concierge appears not to notice him. Unwilling to show himself, he hangs back on the street, waiting for Fulcher to step into the lift. Only when Fulcher is safely rising through the floors does he dare enter. He takes the stairs. It's an effort but he doesn't want to be caught out after hours. Not with her. There's too much at stake.

They drink the first bottle while going over the new colour scheme for the flat. 'I've changed my mind about the design,' she says, tossing aside away the old swatches. 'We don't want to be distracted from our work with flashy colours. White, I would say. Something fresh and functional.'

'White, fresh and functional.' He opens the second bottle and draws his chair close. 'That's me.'

'You're funny!' she says. They knock back their drinks and he laughs as she gags and spurts liquid over herself. She stands up with a yelp. The sight of wet wine on her blouse drives him crazy.

He grabs her hand. 'We shouldn't,' she says. She instinctively looks across at the French doors. It's getting dark.

He rises to his feet. 'I'm not interested in shoulds and shouldn'ts.' They kiss. He turns her with force and bends her over the desk. He grunts as he grapples with her skirt. She bucks and twists, but she doesn't want to escape. The desk feels hard beneath her breasts. He spreads her wide and pushes her face towards the piles of A4 paper, Blu-Tack and Tipp-ex. He clamps his hands over hers and begins to thrust. His nicotine breath is on her neck. He's such a brute. Yes, yes he is. She turns her head, hungry to kiss him as he bears down upon her.

'Oh Bill,' she gasps, 'Bill! Bill!'

The sound of this name startles him. It sounds strange and unfamiliar. He almost stops but his lust has too much momentum. The Page 3 girl on the wall beams encouragingly. Sweat prickles on his moustache. The soft explosions of his heart pound in his ears.

'Debbie!' he cries. 'Debbie!'

Debbie must be her name, he tells himself as he slumps, panting, next to her. Of course it is. Debbie is his little lovely. His little secret.

*

She's guiltily silent as she pulls up her knickers. He wipes perspiration from his neck with the back of his hand and takes a slug from the bottle. The pounding in his head grows louder, more intense. The rain rages against the French doors. An excruciating creak permeates the room, as if something is being hauled up on a winch.

The phone rings. They stare at it. Wait for it to stop.

'It's after hours,' he says, thinking fearfully about the figure on the towpath. 'We don't need to answer it.'

'It might be important.' She can't help herself. She picks up the receiver. 'Hello?'

Static hisses from the handset. Faint bleeps punctuate the white noise. It could be a voice speaking, trying to get through, but she's not sure. She puts the handset down.

'The line's faulty. Let me check it.' She dials 123.

The voice is clear: 'At the third stroke it will be 6:39 and thirteen seconds . . . '

Beep, Beep, Beep.

'At the third stroke it will be 6:35 and two seconds . . . '

Beep, beep, beep.

'At the third stroke it will be 5.45 and 50 seconds . . . '

Beep, beep, beep.

She throws the receiver at the wall.

'What are you doing?' he hisses. 'What's wrong with you?'

There's a knock at the door.

'Now look what you've done . . . you – you stupid cow.'

He immediately feels sorry for saying it. She looks so sweet and vulnerable. He strokes her hair, murmurs that he loves her. She forgives him. It's not his fault. They're both in this together and a man like him has so much more to lose. She touches his lips with her finger and says, 'Sssh, Bill. I'll tell him you're not here.'

He slumps onto a chair and grabs the wine bottle, mouthing the name 'Debbie' over and over, wondering why it seems wrong. She tiptoes through the hall and stares through the peephole. The corridor is empty but the knocking continues. She realises the sound is no longer coming from this door, but from their living room – from outside the window.

The drink has made him giddy. It feels like he's on the deck of an old galleon as he stands up and sways toward the French windows. The glass vibrates with each knock, harder and harder until can bear it no longer. He grips the handle of the door.

'Please don't,' she says from the back of the room.

Suddenly he understands what's been lurking out there at night, watching him, but more importantly, watching *her*. He knows who it is and why he's so angry. 'I don't care if he's out there.'

'Please, Bill. No.'

'This has to stop.'

What the hell was he thinking? A man in his position, with a factory to run, his every move scrutinised by Fulcher, that miserable weasel boss of his. They were crazy to think this affair would work. It's too late now. They must face the consequences. He yanks down on the handle and steps onto the balcony.

The Navigation seethes with rain. Explosions boom across the marsh. Veins of light crackle between the pylons. The cloud is so low it drifts through the street-lamps, coughing florets of vapour towards the pavement. A knot of dense blackness, shrouded in yellow light, moves slowly out from under the bridge.

'You want me?' he shouts. 'Here I am. You caught me red-handed. She's with me now.'

He drains the bottle and hurls it over the balcony. As it strikes the water the building shakes. The blackness forms the shape of a man, pointing at him, shouting something he can't make out. His outline dissolves and spills over the canal's edge, turning the water into a pitch slick. With a roar it erupts like a geyser, high above the balcony. Two headlamp eyes open in the billowing blackness and glare at him. With a cry of terror he tumbles into the living room, drenched and shaking. She tries to stop him as he heads for the front door.

'No! You're too drunk! Please!'

He shrugs her away. 'I'm going down there to have it out.'

'You don't know what he's like.'

'To hell with him.'

There's too much adrenaline in his veins to wait for the lift. The stairs will do. He ignores the concierge's yell as he races through the lobby and onto the Homerton Road. Beams of light from oncoming cars dance at his feet as he weaves across the bridge. He slips onto his back on the wet steps, blood flowering on his white shirt, but he feels no pain as he staggers down the final steps, where he turns and sees nothing but wet brick.

This can't be! He slaps at the wall in a fury. This can't be, this can't be, this can't be.

A sharp crack spins him on his heels. Matchmaker Wharf flickers like a decaying film reel. One by one, from left to right, the multi-coloured panels on the exterior flip over and turn grey. Gradually another building assumes its shape. A factory, lights blazing from every window. A sign over the loading bay reads **Lesney Industries Ltd.** A hook suspended beneath it swings with a rusty creaking groan, back and forth, back and forth.

There's a crash of steel. A flurry of shouts and calls. Hundreds of doors slamming and lights switching off. A Mexican wave of blackouts begins to darken the façade, row after row, until only a single illuminated window remains. Their bedroom window. Her face is in it. She stares out from the factory, hands planted against the glass, desperately searching the towpath for him.

He points, waves, shouts. Someone approaches behind her. It's not Fulcher. It's someone else. Someone is in the room with her. She hasn't noticed. Goddamn it. She can't see. She can't see the darkness rise up the walls and ooze across the ceiling. He screams out her name. 'Sanjana! Sanjana! Sanjana!'

For a brief second she spots him and smiles. Then blackness consumes her. The light goes out. The factory falls silent. There's only the rain now and the hiss of tires on the wet road above. Alone beneath the bridge he stares up at the window and trembles with rage.

XII

Time's Apostates

London is dreaming again. Her fingers claw at the bedposts. She groans on sweat-drenched sheets as it all comes back to her. It's 1940. The black gulls of the Luftwaffe flock over the East End. The air screams as incendiary bombs light the sky, raining fire, turning the river to smoke. Garrulous cockneys shake their fists at their ceilings. 'If you take my house, then you can bleedin' well take me too, Mr Hitler.'

In a mutilated Hackney street a hand bursts from a mound of rubble and finds the grip of a fire warden. The warden recognises the emerging face. It's his old school headmaster. 'Phippsy. Well I'll be blowed.' They stagger down the street together, laughing, as shrapnel whizzes over their heads. In Anderson Shelters families huddle around tins of Spam and sing 'Roll Out the Barrel'. When the smoke clears the next morning a milkman skips through the debris, business as usual madam, stepping past boys playing 'Battle of Britain heroes' with planes carved from shattered window frames.

This is London's narcissistic lie-dream, a narrative in which the obedient London masses remained plucky in the face of annihilation. Her brain has sealed off the neural pathways which carry memories of panic, blind fear and self-interest. They are abandoned tube stations deep in her subconscious, sealed tombs with no public access. London's psyche is nourished instead by a network of self-perpetuating Blitz memes, popular fiction and state-generated propaganda.

One such story tells of how, on the night of the 12th September 1940, the bomb doors of a Heinkel opened over London and a 1000kg explosive device whistled through the hatch. Seconds later it lay embedded in the pavement of Deans Yard, St Paul's Cathedral. Fortunately for the cathedral, the explosion mechanism did not activate on impact. The bomb's deadly potential remained a secret cloaked in steel. Time tick-tocked.

Lieutenant Bob Davies arrived at the scene with his disposal team to find the bomb lodged thirty feet deep in the earth. Tongues of fire licked from a gas main nearby. Sirens howled as Davies and his right hand man, Sapper George Cameron Wylie, set to work. It took them three days to lift the bomb from the crater and lash it to the back of a truck.

The story goes that Davies insisted on driving alone to Hackney Marsh. Roads were cleared as Davies drove the bomb eastward. There the deadly cargo was detonated, leaving a crater 100ft wide, throwing an arc of mud across the warehouses on the other side of the Lee Navigation.

Hackney Marsh's loss was Britain's gain. The cathedral was saved. Thanks to Lieutenant Bob Davies and his team London proved her mettle. She could take whatever was thrown at her. The *Daily Mail* used Davies' tale to galvanise the nation. 'A story that must win a man a VC' screamed the headline. Of course, stories in The *Daily Mail* are never as straightforward as they appear. Davies and Wylie won the George Cross, their achievement splashed across the newspapersas testimony to Britain's Blitz spirit. But it was later revealed that Davies hadn't personally driven the bomb to Hackney Marshes. Then there was the little matter of his sideline activities. In 1942 Davies was found guilty of theft and embezzlement while acting as a bomb disposal officer. He'd extorted cash from the owners of wrecked properties and wrote fraudulent cheques for sums of money he didn't have.

When Davies diffused a bomb in midst of fiery tumult he didn't ask to become a poster boy for the Blitz. Now he was to be written out of the narrative entirely. He went to jail for 18 months. His war was over.

For the marshes this was only one episode in the Blitz story, in which they played a crucial role hosting anti-aircraft guns. Throughout the war trucks came to Hackney Marsh to dump shrapnel and the remains of destroyed houses. The rubble raised the ground level and drained the marsh enough to lay down a vast network of football pitches which would become the spiritual home of Sunday League football.

The players today are unlikely to spare a thought for the graveyard of masonry beneath their feet. They don't think about Lieutenant Bob Davies, a hero and a thief who came here in 1940 to blow up a bomb and save a fictional London. Why should they? The function of drainage is to remove that which bogs us down, not to let it fester on the surface. When it rains on Hackney Marsh the water seeps though a layer of brick, bone and smashed crockery into underground streams, muddy with the filth of history.

*

During the Blitz the majority of Londoners remained resolute in the midst of extraordinary violence. They took their punishment. Many lived to tell the tale in documentaries, books and websites. Those who died in the inferno took their stories with them.

Then there were those who panicked and fled.

As night descended in 1940, ghostly figures emerged from Hackney's blacked-out streets, pushing their belongings in prams and carts across the marshes. They were known as trekkers. They didn't want to hide beneath the stairs or squeeze into an Anderson Shelter. Instead they made nightly journeys to Hackney Marshes and Epping Forest to sit out the bombing raids. They felt safer in a big open space than in the city. Yes, the state may have gone to war with Nazi Germany. Perhaps there was a just reason for it, too. But they weren't going to sit there like good citizens and wait to be buried alive.

The government tried to whitewash trekkers from the wartime story. Newsreels ignored them. They spoiled the 'London Can Take It' narrative – starring fearless, sing-along-a-cockney heroes and stiff-upper-lipped toffs – which they were cultivating as a psychological defence against the Germans. The idea of terrified Londoners fleeing to the woods with their prized possessions was an affront to the bulldog spirit. It simply wasn't cricket.

In the end it was easy to pretend the trekkers weren't there. There were no film crews on the marshes. No press. No pubs. No conduits through which their tales could travel. When trekkers stepped over the river, they exited the narrative. It's for this reason that many people still come here for refuge today. You can find sleeping bags and ground sheets strewn in the thickets. A duvet cover draped like a baroque curtain on the branch of a tree, bottles ranged round scorched campfire sites, plastic bags full of shit-caked toilet roll dangling from the railings.

In February 2012 a large blue tent appeared among the trees in the Middlesex Filter Beds. It had a raised wooden floor with shoes racked in the gap beneath. Outside the door flaps was a scattering of belongings – water bottle, plastic carrier bag and a hat hung on a stick. Day by day their belongings spread across the filter bed. A clothes line was slung between two tree trunks. A kettle dangled over a scorched fireplace. By the entrance was a wheeled suitcase of the sort businessmen drag through airports. Soon they established their own settlement among the trees. It was admirably brazen. With its information signs, lockable gates and art installations, the Middlesex and Essex nature reserves are the few areas of the marshes which are defined tourist attractions. Yet these people had simply decided to move in.

Hendrix and I were walking through the filter beds the day the culprits were caught by the authorities and told to leave. A couple in their late twenties yelled at each other in an Eastern European language as they plucked their belongings off the clothes line. In the plateau at the centre of the filter beds a Lea Valley ranger tapped his fingers on his vehicle's steering wheel, the engine humming.

Hendrix felt nothing, for he was a dog and almost wholly preoccupied with sniffing secret messages encoded in piss. I was sad to see the campers go. For that blink of an eye in the filter beds' history, this makeshift tent harked back to the trekkers of the Blitz and, long before that, a time when prehistoric humans lived and hunted by the River Lea. When I returned home I wrote a story about what London might look like, post apocalypse: overgrown ruins populated by tribes dwelling in makeshift tarpaulin tents, boiling water from the flooded marshes. The marshland was a wild place existing outside a silver walled city of technology, where outcasts lived by their wits among the ruins, selling old books, musical instruments and fragments of human ephemera. I had a lot to thank the blue tent people for, but they had vanished into the mists of time. I would never see them again.

In the 21st century the marshes remain a lure for people on the run from whatever ails them in their city life. Once you cross the canal from Hackney there are no security cameras. No streetlights. No advertising billboards. No synagogues, churches or mosques. No schools. No property. The state loses its power here. Traditional communication lines are severed. Here it's possible to live – for a moment at least – liberated. You can establish your own networks, create your own story.

This manifests itself as an urge for the marshes' users to write themselves onto the landscape, either through the repeated use of an area for a specific activity – camping, drug taking, drinking, meditation, dancing, sex – or literally, in the form of graffiti. There's a freedom of narration possible in these hinterlands which transcends that faux freedom, characteristic of the city, which offers you only a choice between available products. Instead of 'Which of these things would you like?' the marshland asks, 'What would you like this place to be?'

There's only one thing that stops modern trekkers being truly free – the tyranny of sound. The city might be forced to halt at the Lea's edge, but what London cannot turn to concrete, tarmac and steel, she colonises with noise, like a propaganda broadcast blasted through a Tannoy by a foreign force preparing to invade.

As you escape across the river to a landscape of woodland and scrub, the noises of London are made more acute by the contrast between what you hear and what you see. Motor engines, power lines and aeroplanes drone through the rushes. The percussion of hammer on steel, slow-moving trains and crunching gears shakes the trees. A tidal wash of traffic noise ebbs and flows with the wind. Shouts drift through the brambles: obscure dog names, builders' banter, loud arguments on mobile phones. Children's laughter rings in the hollows. A goose opens its beak and honks an ambulance siren. Verdant verges speak with the voices of railway workers. Leaves crackle with AM Radio. Magpie cackles blend with the crunch of shifting gears and the thud of pallets.

This is most emphatic in the Wick Woodland, a popular place for trekkers to camp out and drink away their burdensome selves. This dense triangle of wood alongside the Lee Navigation is separated from Hackney Marsh by the Homerton Road. Its fate diverged from that of its neighbour after the Second World War, when it was spared the dumping of Blitz rubble. This made it a prime target for developers, who were held off until 1991 when the M11 Link Road (now the A12) was built across the bottom of Wick Field, its Ballardian flyover sweeping over the Lea and down towards Temple Mills. In compensation the community was promised that Wick Field would become public woodland, planted with a wide variety of trees to encourage diverse wildlife. The woods were not simply an eye-pleasing gift to placate locals for yet another intrusion on the marshes. They fulfilled a vital function, cushioning residents and marsh users from the worst of the road noise.

Entering the woodland, you step inside a vast, organic sound filter, channelling the dissonant resonances of concrete and tarmac. At the fringe of the wood the A12 roars like a distant ocean but the volume swells as you progress down sinewy paths through ash, silver birch, hawthorn, rowan, hazel, yew and oak. You can detect a symphony of micro-melodies and rhythms within the wash of noise: the sound of tyres on road like strings, the timpani rumble of lorries and cymbal clash of gears changing and mechanisms of battered white vans rattling. Standing among the still trees, it's like listening to a BBC library LP of traffic noise in the middle of the countryside.

The first people to settle in this sound chamber were travellers. They came in 1999, much to the chagrin of locals, who accused them of flytipping rubbish and promptly evicted them. Since then, settlers have been more discreet. They leave only fragments. The remains of fires. Abandoned bivouacs leaned against trees, littered with wrappers, coke bottles and crisp bags. Downward arrows and a triangle daubed onto a tree trunk in white paint are 'tramp code', secret messages left for others who camp out here. A DIY drinker's bench constructed from two stumps and a couple of branches is surrounded by Kronenbourg cans. Elsewhere there are hints at more obscure activities: a sparkly child's trainer upturned in a bush, a pair of bright yellow shop mannequin's feet half way up a tree, a breezeblock chiselled at the corners, the beginnings of a sculpture. When you're alone in these woods the omnipresent chugging drone of the A12 transforms the mundane into the arcane. An effigy made from twigs, twisted into a bunch, seems the work of a Blair Witch. The wings of a blackbird on the path are attached to each other by bloodied cartilage, but there's no bird in between. A human-length mound of earth beneath a tree is scattered with shattered brick and shreds of blue plastic, petals at a grave. A yellow 'no parking or waiting' sign from the long-demolished Lesney factory is warped and scorched black from fire.

The process of coppicing in the woodland means that some areas are fenced off. The trees within are hacked down to knee-height, their branches burned. Their bulbous stumps are like the skulls of triceratops in a post-meteor landscape. Some of the marshland might have looked like this in 1940 when Hitler's fire rained, the anti-aircraft guns boomed and Lieutenant Bob Davies struggled with the St Paul's bomb. On some days flames can still be seen here and so too can the trekkers of old, hauling their belongings, tormented by the city, desperate to escape. The morning after their refuge in the woodland, when the earth steams, litter is scattered on the dead leaves but the trekkers have gone.

After a while a man comes walking with his cocker spaniel, looking for clues.

XIII

Ursus Rising

'I'll bloody kill you,' her husband says. 'You filthy whore.'

'Richard,' she begs. 'Please . . . '

He squeezes Jean's neck, forcing her backwards over the sink. His shadow oozes across the ceiling as he looms above her, breath rank with Old Holborn and whisky. If she'd known he'd been drinking she never would have started a conversation. She can't remember what she said to anger him. Whatever it was, she's sorry. But she can't say it. Her words are trapped between his fingers.

'You aint worth a fuck in a ditch.' Richard punches Jean hard in the face, lets her drop to the linoleum. He thrusts his knee into her ribcage. She curls into a tight ball, holding her cry inside.

Air raid sirens howl.

'Now look what you done!' Richard strides from the kitchen. She peers up. George is under the table playing with his teddy. She smiles at him through tears. Gives him a wave.

Richard reappears with a kit bag slung over his shoulder. 'I'm off down the marsh. You can take your little bastard to the

Anderson. Oh, and close them curtains or the warden'll give you another slap.'

The kitchen door rattles shut. His Dunkirk limp clumps through the yard. When she hears the back gate creak she gets up and splashes water on her throbbing jaw. The blackout blankets are piled in the larder. There isn't time to put them up by herself.

'Come with Mummy.' Jean stretches under the table to grasp George's tiny hand. She scoops him up, wincing with pain, and carries him through the house, turning off the lamps and closing curtains. Before she flicks off the bedroom light she catches her reflection in the dressing table mirror. Her face is grotesquely swollen. She can't possibly go to the Anderson Shelter looking like this. Not again. She's run out of excuses. She'll have to sit this one out with George.

In a crescendo of bomber noise, Jean feels her way through the pitch black, cooing 'Twinkle Twinkle Little Star'. She reaches behind the kitchen door for the Mickey Mouse gas mask and straps it to George's head.

'Mickey time!' she says.

There's a cupboard under the stairs, scattered with cushions and toy blocks. Jean puts George inside. 'Mummy will be there in a moment.'

Jean goes to the front room and stares out at the searchlights dancing in the sky. Explosions crackle across London. They live so close to the Lea she can hear the whip-crack of anti-aircraft guns on the marsh. Trembling, she draws the curtains and fumbles her way to the sideboard. Nested in a box full of darning wool is her secret stash of Players Navy Cuts. She lights one with trembling hands and slumps into the armchair. In the din of falling bombs she begins to sob.

A series of explosions rattles the plates on the dresser. Flame

erupts from the row of houses on Oswald Street behind. Black smoke belches across the backyards. A gust blows open the unlatched kitchen door and the linoleum blushes red with the fiery glare. A beast as wide as the doorframe slowly drags itself into the kitchen, ribs jutting from piebald brown fur, shredded jaws dripping with blood, tongue lolling. An eyeball dangles on its cheek. The other is yellow and wide. Paw by paw, it inches across the floor, wheezing for breath in the curling smoke tendrils, drawn by the smell it seeks. Driven from its home on the marsh, it is starving.

The beast heaves onto its hind legs and crashes its paws on the table. A heel of stale bread and a tin of Spam flip into the air and clatter to the floor. It slurps up the bread and begins to gnaw at the tin. A tooth punctures metal. It tries to swallow but the tin is stuck to its teeth. The beast shakes its head and the tin skitters under the oven.

There's another scent. Stronger, more alluring.

The beast slopes into the hall. It senses life squirming in the darkness. Something beneath the stairs. It claws at the door, carving deep grooves, until the wood splinters and shatters. George in his Mickey Mouse gas-mask hugs his knees in terror. The creature opens its jaws.

A piercing scream startles the beast. 'Leave us alone!'

A metallic object thuds onto the back of its head. With a howl it jerks back, cracking its skull against the door frame. It turns to face its attacker. Panting heavily, Mrs Jean Chilcott stands in the hall, glowing red in the firelight, clutching a coal shovel in one hand and a poker in the other. The beast rears up on its hind legs.

'To hell with you, Richard.' Jean swipes upwards with the coal shovel, slicing the beast's neck. An arc of blood spatters onto George's Mickey Mouse gas mask. The beast's head tilts back as if hinged.

With a shriek, Jean rams the poker through its rib cage. The beast's emaciated skin tears like paper. Noiselessly it staggers sideways and topples into the kitchen. It twitches on the floor, blood gurgling in its lungs, hind leg bicycle-kicking the air. Jean stoops into the stair cupboard, clutching George close to her, crying now, not holding it in anymore, just crying until it all comes out.

'Sorry,' she says. 'Sorry, sorry, sorry.'

When the bomb strikes their roof it takes everything – masonry, crockery, linen, family photos, diaries, memory and life itself – down into the pit. All that's left is smoke and the wail of sirens in the night.

*

A week later, little Albie Moxley tells everyone he's found a bear's paw in the rubble at the bottom of Millfields Road. Moxley is the local dunce, a fat kid who's always talking nonsense. They don't believe him anymore than they believe Susan Fripp when she sees a crocodile in the Lea River in December 1940. No more is said about the matter. Eventually the trucks come to collect the debris of number 86 and dump it on Hackney Marsh.

XIV

Beasts of the Cryptoforest

On the 27th of December 1981, four boys leave their homes to play on the snow. In this weather, Hackney Marsh becomes an irresistible plateau of bright white possibility. They build snowmen. They throw snowballs. They do what young boys do. When they find a mysterious set of footprints, they follow, wondering what could possibly make such huge impressions.

Thirteen-year old Tommy Murray is walking ahead of his friends when he comes upon something which, at first glance, he thinks is a dog. But this creature is big. It rears up at him, growling, all teeth and claws. Tommy screams. His friends' jaws open in disbelief. *It's a bear*. The boys run screaming through the snow and don't stop until they reach home.

An archived radio report from the time reveals that, in interviews with Inspector Dave Jordan of Hackney Police, the boys – Tommy Murray, Darren Willoughby and Elliot Sanderson – describe a 'giant great growling hairy thing', almost six feet tall. This sort of tale usually gets short shrift from the authorities, but there's a bigger, grizzlier picture to consider. Three weeks previously, the headless, skinned bodies of two bears were found floating in the River Lea. Rumours say that local circuses have been feuding and that these bears were murdered as an act of retribution. Perhaps they weren't circus bears at all. Who knew what really lurked in the deepest recesses of the marsh?

Given the recent Hackney bear deaths, the police are inclined to believe the boys' story. Track marks further convince them. Fifty police officers pour onto the marsh with sniffer dogs and horses. Marksmen load up. A helicopter buzzes the skies. They scour the marshes for three days. They discover more prints in the snow and a smashed allotment shed, but no beast.

Later, a man called Ron tells *The Sun* newspaper that he's the bear. He got the idea to dress up when the dead bear story hit the local news a few weeks before. But his claim isn't taken seriously enough for rumours to die down. This wasn't an isolated incident. There were sightings of beasts on the marsh before this event, and there have been since.

According to *Fortean Times* writer Tina Wrath a 'bear-like animal' was spotted on the marshes in the 1970s. She claims that fossils of prehistoric bears have been found in the Lea Valley. To compound the myth, an episode of the comedy TV series *The Detectives*, starring Jasper Carrot and Robert Powell, broadcast in 1997, based its plot on the bear story. 'The Beast of Hackney Marshes' features the detectives staking out the woodlands to capture a prankster who is dressing up as a bear to frighten locals. The twist in the tale is that, after they apprehend the culprit, they confront a real-life bear. An approximation of hilarity ensues. Credits roll. And so the beast snuffled its way into the annals of British light entertainment.

In November 2008 a bear sighting in Hollow Ponds was reported in the *Walthamstow Guardian*. Not strictly on Hackney

Marshes, this small area of woodland is only two miles east of the 1981 sighting. *The East London & Wessex Guardian* ran with the headline: 'Is "bigfoot" on the loose in the woods?' Fitness instructor Michael Kent told the local newspaper:

'I looked over and saw this strange, dark figure that resembled a bear. It was hunched over and I could see it had a really hairy back. I think it must have heard me and scampered off into the bushes after a couple of seconds. It was getting dark but I still managed to get a good look at it. It was about 4ft tall, so it was too small to be human, but not the right shape to be a deer . . . '

These are only the stories which hit the headlines. It's likely that many other walkers have seen something strange in the environs of the marshes. If you scour the internet for blogs and articles about beast sightings you can find comments beneath the posts relating other stories. This is an example, written in a bizarre Riddley Walker dialect:

. . . end of september 2009 on an early morning approx 5 am was walking dog on hackney marsh near river wen i saw a figure bout 7 ft tall furry very wide, run beside me and dog . . . it wasnt human . . . dog chased it . . . luckily dog came bak, scared me like hell, definitly some sort of bear like creature

Other reports claim that a four foot tall sabre tooth tiger has been seen prowling the marshes. Geoff Challis, a reader commenting on an article in the *Marshman Chronicles* blog, tells this story:

'Back in 1977 or `78, myself and a couple of friends came across some odd remains in the marshes. This was in the area beyond the railway at the end of Coppermill Lane E17. It was later reported in the local paper (*Guardian*) that the carcasses of several large cats (Lions and Tigers etc) had been found in the marshes. I am unsure of the exact date, but it was very foggy I recall, absurdly like a scene from an old Hammer horror film.'

On May 17th 2012 the *Hackney Gazette* reported another sighting of the 'Beast of Hackney Marsh' and included a photograph of a black shape in the undergrowth. The picture was taken by university student Helen Murray as she strolled by the Old River Lea. She told the *Gazette*: 'I tried to stay calm as I wasn't sure what kind of animal it was or if it was even alive . . . I had my phone ready to call 999. Then the creature moved. Somehow I managed to take a couple of pictures before I ran.'

In a weird denouement, this animal turned out to be Willow, a Newfoundland dog owned by Paul Winter, the drummer from `90s Britpop band Kula Shaker. The *Hackney Gazette* reported that Willow could reach a height of over 5ft when standing on her hind legs. However, when shown a picture of Willow in her most bearish pose, Helen Murray told the newspaper, 'I'm pretty sure it wasn't a dog as it was far too big. And its build wasn't dog-like.'

At the bottom of the article on the *Gazette*'s website, headlined 'Beast of Hackney Marshes – Has Kula Shaker Drummer Solved the Mystery?' the newspaper asks readers this question: 'Is Willow the beast of Hackney Marsh or does something else stalk the area?'

A single comment below reads: 'A LOT OF RARE ANIMALS ESCAPED BEING SMUGGLED IN BY BOAT OVER THE YEARS.'

This settles the matter nicely.

*

The *Gazette*'s reader might be correct. Travelling zoos, circuses and private animal collectors make it plausible that unexpected creatures such as caiman, wild cats and venomous snakes could live in urban areas. This is why the sighting of a lion roaming Essex in 2012 was taken seriously enough by the local police force to spark an expensive big cat hunt which gripped the news headlines in Britain for many days. Of course, deeper psychological forces could be at play. It could be that the peculiar atmosphere of the East End's marshlands inspires this impression that wild beasts lurk in the undergrowth.

Cryptozoological sightings tend to occur in liminal zones: on the borderlands of human habit and wilderness, at the point between night and day, in unsettled mental states. Hackney and Walthamstow Marshes provide the ideal conditions. They exist in multiple chronological and sociological states. This is a pasture land, sewerage system, electricity hub, flood plain, nature reserve, sports ground and an illicit space where people indulge in sexual and narcotic acts. You can see the weathered sediments of history exposed in a landscape which looks very much like a future when humankind is gone, the waters are rising, and vegetation has begun to reclaim the masonry. In this way the marshland is a cryptoforest, a term used by Wilfried Hou Je Bek, author of the website *Cryptoforesty*, to describe those areas in a city where nature has been, deliberately or accidentally, allowed to flourish. Examples include vegetation on a roundabout, overgrown back alleys, and those avenues of trees beside motorways and railway lines. He writes:

Cryptoforests are sideways glances at post-crash landscapes, diagrammatic enclaves through which future forest cities reveal their first shadows, laboratories for dada-do-nothingness, wild-type vegetable free states, enigma machines of uncivilized imagination, psychogeographical camera obscuras of primal fear and wanton desire, relay stations of lost ecological and psychological states.

The Lower Lea Valley's stretches of old river and marshland intimate a time before humans sculpted the landscape, when they were at one with the seasons, living off the land, competing with animals for food. Sometimes zombie fragments of these lost states rise from the bog. A Bronze Age dug-out canoe and the remains of a thirteen feet long Saxon boat from A.D. 950-1000 have been found in Walthamstow Marshes. Today the hunched figures of narrowboat dwellers chopping logs on the waterside echo the lives of our ancestors. Plumes of black smoke rise from human fires on the marsh as they would have done three thousand years ago.

*

Humans are not the only mammals to haunt the marshes. Over the ridge of aqueduct path behind Leyton and Walthamstow Marshes, horses stand in a field beneath the humming pylons. They are distant relatives of those animals which once galloped here with flowing manes and thundering hooves, their Iron Age riders whooping with the thrill of the chase.

These are tired modern horses, unpaid employees of the Lea Valley Riding School. A dappled mare circles a trainer in the paddock as ponies stare bleakly from a row of stables. A stallion is tethered to a fence, steam wisping from his nostrils. In a field alongside the railway lines where a stalled freight train rumbles, two horses break into a run then, almost as soon as they start, abandon the chase and go their separate ways. Sometimes a horse

will be taken from the riding school and led through the marshes at walking pace. The jumbles of dung they leave on the trail steam gently in the autumn air, their stench a portal to a lost London when horses suffered a series of humiliations as the city came shambling into the countryside like a boisterous student.

In 1735 a bizarre swimming race was held between two horses on the marshes. They cut through the waters of the Lea, ears flat back against their heads, eyes wild, the drunken shouts of men and women rising from the banks. This was English countryside at the time. The horses weren't accustomed to being used as low-rent entertainment. This impertinent treatment was the first sign of an advancing culture more devastating than the Danish Viking marauders who once sailed up this river. The dirty, bawdy, lascivious, city of London was on the cusp of an extraordinary expansion.

Thirty years later, the industrial revolution turned London into an international powerhouse. Horses were put to work pulling barges piled with brick, overcrowded omnibuses full of commuters and high-speed postal carriages. By 1900 there were approximately 50,000 horses working for London's transport network. After the Second World War, there was a knacker's yard on Middlesex Wharf by the Lea Bridge. The blood of disposed horses would flow beneath the fencing and into the river. Hackney resident and local memoirist, Brian Walker, recalls that for a prank some of the workers cut off a couple of horses' heads and stuck them on poles so that they stared out at travellers crossing the Lea Bridge. He writes:

'Not many people saw the funny side of this thoughtless prank, in fact a report in the *Hackney Gazette* said that passengers on buses were physically sick, children screamed with fright and one unfortunate individual fainted, splitting his head open.'

With the rising popularity of the motorcar, the horse tide went out again. The only horses seen in the city centre today are those ridden by police during festivals and riots. The animals of the Lea Valley nature reserve are like stranded crabs in a rock pool. They chase each other in circles on the frosty clay and blink at shrieking children.

*

The true beasts of the Lower Lea are found on Walthamstow Marsh, the hunting grounds of kestrels and herons. An elevated duckboard walkway stretches through a fenced enclosure where the grass been left to grow long and wild. You don't see them at first. They hide like Asian water buffalo beside a flooded V2 bomb crater. It's only when you peer closely that you notice a brown back. Then another. Then the curly horns.

Here is the cow sanctuary, where rare breed Black Dexter, English Longhorn and Belted Galloways stalk the rushes.

There's something magical about seeing cows in the inner city, framed by waterfront flats and the distant silhouettes of the Gherkin, Shard and Heron Towers. It's a strange union of here and there, cow and skyscraper, futures and pasts. Next to their field is the arch of a railway bridge where, in 1909, Alliot Verdon Roe built an aeroplane. Roe was a doctor's son from Salford. After years working on the rails and sailing the high seas he set his mind on becoming the first Briton to build and fly a plane on British soil. The *Daily Mail* gave him £75 as second prize in their model aeroplane competition. On the July 23rd he wheeled his Roe 1 triplane, nicknamed *The Yellow Terror*, from under the arch.

The 9hp JAP engine rasped. The plane bumped and rattled. There was a gasp as it lifted off the ground. The plane buzzed low over the marsh like a paper dragonfly. Almost as soon as it was up, it came down. But the flight was long enough to make it official.

Roe stepped from the plane a hero. He not only had Walthamstow Marsh at his feet, but his entire future. The foundation of the AVRO aeronautical company. The construction of Lancaster bombers. Thousands of planes in the sky over Europe. Dresden burning. Germany screaming. His own sons perishing in a war he helped to equip. The burial mounds of Leyton and Hackney Marshes. His cheerleading the politics of Oswald Mosley. A knighthood. And, at the end of it all, an elderly man cycling backwards on handlebars for the entertainment of his laughing grandchildren.

After the days of Roe it seemed unlikely a cow would ever return to this spot on Walthamstow Marsh. Then on 18 July 2002, ecologist Brian Wurzell found 'three tiny, immature scraps of a plant growing below a ditch-bank'. This turned out to be only one of two British colonies of an endangered plant called creeping marshwort. This ecological breakthrough didn't quite make the national headlines but botanists were cock-a-hoop. Wurzell and the Lea Valley Regional Park authority drew up an action plan for protecting the plant, which included the re-introduction of cattle to the marsh in 2003. Today they graze on the dominant grasses so the weaker marshwort gets its place in the sun. The hollows carved out by the cow's hooves create new opportunity for this plant to spread and flourish. And so the prodigal cows have returned to their ancient pasture land.

In the countryside locals tend to treat cows as part of the topographical furniture and pay them scant attention. But in East London visitors react as if they've seen mythical creatures. 'Look! There it is. A cow! A cow in London! Just look at those horns!'

When the cattle are moved out of the enclosed field into open areas of Walthamstow Marsh, life gets uglier for them. Outside their fenced sanctuary humans can roam freely. Teenagers chase them across the field, waving sticks. Unleashed dogs run yapping circles round them. This is nothing new. As far back as 1865 commoners complained that the influx of visitors from the city was upsetting the cattle. The Victorian livestock might have been spooked, but these inner city breeds are tough. There is a far greater chance you'll get murdered by a cow out here than by a bear.

*

On a crisp February day in 2011, I pushed through the gate by A.V Roe's arch and followed Hendrix over the clod. A small herd of cows lingered near the railway line with their calves. I calmly put Hendrix on the lead. Hendrix had been half-blind with cataracts since birth. He was unbothered by horses and cows. They appeared to him as blurred nodes on a shadowy landscape. Even up close they were nothing more than a smell he found curious, but less exciting than that of a discarded kebab, which I had unfairly banned him from eating. But on this day, it was the cows which came to Hendrix.

As the wedge of marsh between the railway and woodland narrowed to a triangle, two of the more curious calves ambled towards Hendrix. I tensed as they came to within a few feet, blocking their progress. Hendrix strained forward, sniffing the air, as the calves pushed their noses towards his. There was a moment of peace between we three species. Then I heard a violent snort. I turned to see two adults approaching from behind in a raptor-like ambush.

Clever girls.

The cows barreled forwards and Hendrix disappeared beneath their gargantuan heads. Crying out, I heaved at the lead, dragging the dog from beneath the cows. I dashed between the two calves, dragging a wheezing, spluttering Hendrix behind me. The adults charged again but now Hendrix and I were racing across the marsh, picking up speed, teeth bared to the wind. The cows lost interest, assembling in a row, placidly chewing the cud – or perhaps tobacco, you never know with these East London cows.

You don't mess with the beasts of the cryptoforest.

XV

Marsh Meat

Ever since he found the bear paw sticking out from the rubble of Mr and Mrs Chilcott's house, days after his ninth birthday, in that fiery year of 1940, Albie Moxley liked to find things. Coins, shoes, false teeth, pipes, old photographs. Even when the bombs stopped falling there were rich pickings across the river, on Hackney Marsh, where trucks tipped smoking debris every day, and the air stank of battery acid. He found smashed dolls, cigarette boxes and, one time, a whole Bakelite radio casing, like it had come right out of a factory.

But no find was ever quite as thrilling as that bear paw which felt so warm inside his blazer as he hurried to Millfields Park to show the other boys. They laughed in his face and sang a right horrible ditty:

Poxy Moxley
Found a bear but it was only a foxy
And that was the end of fatty, spotty, poxy Moxley

Sobbing, Albie lolloped home on his club foot and hid the paw in a wooden box under his bed. He never showed his treasures to anyone else, not even his dear Mammy. Mammy said it was best not to stir things up by talking to people about things inside his head. Best keep himself to himself. With his tank-driving Daddy dead in North Africa, neighbours muttered that he should go to a hospital for stupid people, but Mammy said it was okay, he had special qualities nobody understood. She kept him at home to do Daddy's work, fixing things and being there for a cuddle, while she went to work at Gibbons furniture store on Amhurst Road to keep the roof over their heads.

After the war there wasn't much doing in the streets of Hackney for an expert finder like Albie Moxley. Instead he would go to the marshes and poke around for treasure in the woods – birds' nests, eggs, feathers, dead crows and the like. He'd bring them home to dry, scrape clean, boil and turn into things that pleased him. A squirrel skeleton on a driftwood surfboard. Pigeon's feet jutting from the eye sockets of a rabbit's head nailed to a rotten cricket bat. Blackbird feathers plastered to a photo of Mammy and Daddy so all you could see were their eyes staring out, coloured with red ink. He sewed a dead dog's tail into a pair of shorts so it looked like a giant hairy man's thingy dangling. That made him chuckle, even though he was twenty-two years old and knew the girls preferred that sort of thing for real. But, as his Mammy said, it was best he kept his thoughts to himself and so he did.

Then in 1967 his Mammy said they needed more money to keep the same roof over their heads and that she knew a feller at the Lesney Matchbox Car factory on the Homerton Road who could get him a proper job. He was to be the Chieftain of the Broom, she announced, beaming, you're going right to the top, Albie. And she was right. He was given his own broom! Every day he'd scutter between the rows of machines, all clackety clacking and thuddumping, sweeping and picking up rubbish. He did it well. After all, he was an expert finder. He got his own special brown coat, though it was a struggle to button it round his tummy. *Ladies, look out!* thought Albie. And they did look out, too. They went right past him, looking out at something else in the distance.

When Mammy was chewed up by cancer in 1974 they moved him into a ground-floor council flat in Sudbury Court, opposite the marsh. There was a right ruckus when they found his cellar full of treasures. 'Like something from Dante's inferno,' one of the social workers said, but Albie didn't know what that meant. All he could think of was Bruce Forsyth on the telly going, 'Dante do well, Dante do well'. They took his treasures and burned them, told him he was lucky they didn't haul him away and that if they caught him with that filth again he'd end up on the street.

Albie didn't like Sudbury Court. It was dirty and noisy, with no cellar or Mammy, and the kids on the stairs called him Spazzer and Mongoloid and Fatty and Munster. They would throw eggs at him and push chips through his letterbox. Rather than walk the gauntlet of taunts to get to Lesney each morning Albie crossed the footbridge to Hackney Marsh and followed the Lee Navigation, keeping an eye out for bones and corpses, rubber jonnies and pornymags. He never took them home these days for fear of losing the roof over his head. The only treasure he had left was kept beneath his bed. That wooden box containing his first and greatest find.

Well, it *was* his greatest ever find. Until one icy December morning in 1981 when he found the bear skins.

The two brown furs were draped over a branch, steaming slightly, shaggy heads oozing needles of blood onto the slush. A crow yanked sinew from one of the eye sockets and another perched on top, picking at the fur. Albie trembled with recognition, the boys' jeers from forty years ago returning to his ears. He shooed away the crows and crouched by one of the paws, touching it tenderly. It looked as beautiful as the day he crawled over the ruins of Mrs Chilcott's house. Tears welled. He had been right all along, there *were* bears in Hackney. They should have believed him. Things would have been different.

His watch said seven-thirty. In half an hour he needed to be at the factory or there would be a right hoo-ha. Albie weighed up his options. There was a hold-all in his flat. If he was quick he could grab these skins for himself before anyone else found them. He would be late for sure and mean Mr Fulcher would give him an earful. But it was a small price to pay for treasures such as these.

Hunched into the cold, Albie Moxley lolloped over the footbridge towards the high rises of Daubeney Green.

*

'What fucking time do you call this?'

Mr Fulcher was all red faced, stomping back and forth with his arms behind his back, harrumphing. He was full of rage lately because of the rumours of the factory closing down. Everyone was talking about it. Fulcher said it was Albie's fault and the likes of him should be locked away with the unionists and the foreigners to leave the hard working people of Britain to get on with fixing the country.

'Was a bit poorly this morning, Mr Fulcher.'

Fulcher peered in disgust at a blood smear on Albie's cheek. 'Well, I fucking hope it's fatal, Moxley. It may as well be, coz when this place goes down who the fuck is going to employ a spastic like you?'

He laughed at that. Fulcher laughed after all his own jokes so that the ladies on the floor could hear him and understand how tough he was.

When Fulcher was done with him, Albie swept the floor, filled the bins, and carried teas to the managers. Every day it was the same. Except today was the Christmas party. Some of the workers wore Santa hats. A few even nodded acknowledgement at him – the ladies too. *Thanks, but no thanks, Ladies*, smirked Albie, thinking of the bear furs hanging in his flat. He hadn't enjoyed Christmas since Mammy died but this year was going to be different. This year he had big plans.

*

The paw seemed so big and unwieldy when he was a little boy. Now when he held it beside the fresh bear skins draped over the shower curtain rail in his bathroom, it looked withered and dry, smaller than he remembered, more human than bear. He gently scratched the furs with it, then put it back in its box and stripped down to his underpants.

Albie turned the electric heater to full blast and began to scrape fat from the back of the skins with a Stanley knife, his belly swinging pendulously with the effort, blobs of flesh spattering the tiles. When he finished he saw his own reflection in the mirror, bald head mottled with bear blood, eyes tired and wrinkled. But his mouth – his mouth was grinning.

Albie unwound some wire coat hangers and threaded them through the bear's front legs, which he splayed into fingers at the wrist. Albie spliced the paws, stretched them around the wires and stitched them together. He hacked the head and paws from the remaining skin, then sewed it to the larger fur as a frontispiece.

It was done. Now all he had to do was go to work every day and be as good as gold until the skins dried out.

It was easy to keep a low profile. There was a weird atmosphere in the factory, even for Christmas, and nobody paid him the slightest bit of attention, not even Fulcher. The men in suits from the offices upstairs came and went in little groups, looking angry or tearful, lighting each other's Superkings and throwing arms around each other's shoulders. Rumours abounded that the factory could close as soon as next year. It was a bad sign that accounts man Bill Ingham and his ever-faithful secretary Debbie were appearing more regularly downstairs. During fag breaks the machinists gossiped that Bob and Debbie were having it off on the marshes. Fulcher would linger near them, talking loudly about himself.

'I don't fucking care what they say, I'm not leaving here,' he said. 'If they close this place I'll fucking stay here and haunt it.' Then he did that laugh again. A few of the ladies joined in but the others looked down and shook their heads. One of them looked at Albie and whispered something to the others, something about 'that poor sod' and he knew they were probably talking about what would happen to him without Mammy or the factory. Little did they know! Albie didn't need anything now that he had the bears of Hackney Marshes. It was only a matter of time.

*

At last, after ten days hanging in the blaze of his electric heater, the skins were dry enough for Albie to take down. He combed them on his bed while watching the Morecambe and Wise Christmas special on his little black and white TV. Ernie and Eric wore top hats and danced a jig with some leggy ladies. Then they went to

bed together. Life was strange in telly land.

At midnight Albie smeared himself in deep heat until he was tingly all over and his winkle stung. He added layers of t-shirts and tracksuit bottoms. Carefully, he folded the bear suit into his holdall and headed to Hackney Marsh. In the woodland he unpacked the bag, lashed the frontispiece across his belly, tethered it with shoe laces and drew down the hollowed-out head so he could peer through the eye holes.

Slowly, he began to walk. The reinforced wire forearms were awkward to swing by his side so he stuck them out in front of him, like Frankenstein's monster. When he reached the football pitches he dropped to all fours. Much better. He shifted the furs into place, then shambled across Hackney Marsh, guided by a crest of light over the trees.

It was surprising how easy it was to run on all fours. No longer his ball and chain, his club foot gave his back-end weight and rhythm, propelling his bulk in great bounds. For a while he circled the goal posts, kicking up ice spray. Then he smelled something sweet and yummy. It drew him towards the old river.

Albie crashed into the tree-line and skittered down an incline towards the river bank. There he sniffed the air, listening. Wings rustled. It was a teal, roosting on a stone ten yards away. He stalked across the mud, breath rasping. The duck shivered. Albie leapt, claws glinting. The bird flapped across the water, leaving him belly-flopped in the slime, trembling with excitement. Next time, Mr Duck, you rascal, next time!

All night Albie ranged along the bushy fringe of the football fields, marvelling at the commotion of birds. *Waaark, waaark.* Hoho! Don't let me catch you crows! He loved the crunch of dead leaves beneath his paws and way the moon shimmered on the frosted branches. He'd never felt more alive since the day of the paw, since that warmth against his heart as he raced through the smoking streets at nine years old, feeling like the world was a wide open mystery for him to piece together. Albie Moxley, the finder.

Only when his limbs began to ache and he slowed to a crawl did Albie finally return to his holdall, stash his suit away and trudge wearily home. Even though it must have been four in the morning, there were kids lingering in the stairwell, blowing smoke rings and drinking from cans, listening to music on a tape recorder that sounded like a thousand razorblades slashing a pig.

'Oi oi fatty!' one of them said, 'Wotchoo been up to ya old perv?'

Albie clutched the holdall tightly as he tried to pass them. The tallest, leanest of the gang blocked his way and stared into his eyes, grinding his jaw. 'Oi - Joey Deacon - can – you – understand - English?'

Then something extraordinary happened which Albie didn't understand at all, and had no control over whatsoever. Without him thinking about it, his left hand jerked upwards into the boy's face, the ends of his fingers hooked at improbable angles, like claws. A roar came from deep inside Albie, so loud and fierce the boy shrank back, startled, slipping onto his arse on the floor. The other kids burst out laughing but the boy remained cowering as Albie shuffled quickly to his flat and closed the door behind him. He flung himself onto his bed and listened in terror as footsteps came right up to the door. A silhouette hovered in the frosted panel, then a nose pressed against it, breath clouding the glass. After a while the footsteps went away.

It was a few hours before Albie's heart calmed down enough for him to sleep.

*

The next day was Christmas Eve, a Friday. Albie slept right through the morning, missing work. He hid in his bathroom all afternoon, dreading a knock from Fulcher or one of his minions. Perhaps they had forgotten him, what with all the Christmas excitement. He guessed not. He guessed that when he started back on Tuesday the 29th, Mr Fulcher would sack him gleefully and that would be the end of it for his career as Chieftain of the Broom, which had made his Mammy so proud. It was sad. But when he looked at the holdall and thought of the frost-bedazzled marsh at night, he was filled with hope and wonder.

He couldn't wait 'til midnight. No sooner had it got dark he wandered out with his holdall. The suit slipped on so easy this time. After a few grunting turns beneath the football posts he ambled towards the Old River, where it felt right for a bear to be. The spoilsport teal kept a safe and respectful distance from him this time. Still, they were worth a shot. Albie placed a tentative paw on a stone and leaned out. A silver streak slithered in the water. Ah, fishy fish, you scrummy little splosher! Albie slashed at the water but he was too slow. Stupid fish.

Albie bounded up the bank to a concrete ridge, intrigued by a malodorous whiff. A line of entrails led to a blackbird corpse, breast split open, head connected by a feathery thread. Angry caws erupted above him and black wings spiralled in the canopy. As Albie clawed at the tree, a rat darted from a dock leaf. Albie plunged after it, snapping his jaws, until he emerged on the football fields. It was amazing. He could see the marsh in newly intricate detail. The movement of water voles traced by the quivering grass tops. The tremble of a branch at an owl's alighting. Streamers of animal scent looked like purple will-o'-the-wisps coiling through the goal posts.

Wild geese flocked overhead, wings creaking. Behind them,

a cormorant, its oily keel catching the moonlight, wheeled away from the geese and down through a gap in the trees. Suddenly it veered up into the sky, twirling like a shuttlecock, and flapped across the playing fields.

Something had spooked the cormorant, and it wasn't him.

Curious and keen to do some super finding, Albie ambled to the gap. He was amazed by what he saw. In the streaked gloom he saw a falcon, perhaps six feet tall, standing with its wings raised, a gold chain around its neck. Beneath its hooked beak a mouth mumbled words Albie couldn't make out. Kneeled before him was another falcon with silvery neck plumage, wings draped suppliantly on the ground. Nearby a tusked tiger sat on its haunches, holding aloft a white sword, a man's face staring out from between its jaws. Albie could see something else beside a tree – a rat, over five foot tall, furiously tugging at its groin. There were other shapes shifting in the darkness on the fringe of the clearing, all rustling and grunting. Their accumulated breath looked like Red Indian smoke signals from the cowboy films he and Mammy used to watch.

The falcon shuffled forwards on her knees, lifting her beak up and away from her face. She wrapped her wings around the standing male and bowed towards his groin. He flung back his head, gasping loudly, 'Ohhhhhhhh.'

Crack.

A twig snapped under Albie's foot. The kneeling falcon turned and Albie glimpsed pale pink boobies swinging beneath her plumage. The male flapped his wings furiously and cried, 'My territory! My territory!' The figures standing around melted back into the darkness while the tiger dropped onto all fours and began to swipe at the surrounding shrub, quickly approaching Albie's hiding spot. With a terrified yelp, Albie bolted along the verge, the tiger snapping through branches in pursuit. It was much faster than him, but didn't seem to want to leave the undergrowth. Seizing his chance, Albie broke across the playing fields, exposed in the moonlight. Halfway across he looked back and saw nothing behind but trembling bushes and the glint of eyes watching him.

*

On Boxing Day, Albie Moxley lay in a hot bath beneath fat-spattered tiles, listening to children clip-clopping down the stairwell with their bikes, Barbie Dolls and Action Men. Afterwards he poured boiling water onto a bowl of noodles but couldn't eat them. He hungered for something far meatier. Instead he sat in bed watching *Gone With the Wind*. He couldn't understand anything about the film. The weirdo accents, red skies and giant houses. Most of all he couldn't understand why it was so complicated between Rhett and Scarlett. Why couldn't they just get down and start doing it right away? All that slamming doors. Running up and down staircases. Twirly dancing. Albie wouldn't know where to begin.

His whole life had been like staring at a television, watching people come and go behind a screen. Albie didn't know what he had seen on Christmas Eve by the Old River, but he had really been there – he could see it, smell it, reach out and touch it. That evening on the marsh had felt closer to living than anything he had experienced in the factory or in the old creaky house with Mammy.

He was desperate to go back.

As midnight approached on the 26th December, 1981, Albie Moxley picked up his holdall and walked out of his council flat into a whirly snow blizzard. White flakes stuck to his eyelashes and it was hard to see. As soon as he crossed the Lee Navigation he pulled on the furs and dropped to all fours. He followed the marsh's northern flank, keeping to the thicket along the perimeter of the Middlesex Filter Beds.

The marsh quickly turned fuzzy white, clouds orange with city light. Feeling exposed, Albie slipped down a steep bank beside a pylon, where the black river swallowed the snow and trees threw shadows. He followed the river to a footbridge, but fear stopped him. He was close to where he'd seen the falcons and tiger. Albie felt jittery, like he was on the threshold of something from which he could never return. Perhaps he should go home. As he clambered back up the bank, snow was so thick on his back that the furs pressed heavy on his body, fusing with his sweat.

Sudbury Court, tall and faded on the horizon, seemed far away now. Closer up, he could see something else. A monstrous dark shape on the playing fields, warping and growing, was moving quickly towards him, closer and closer, until he could hear the squeak of its paws on fresh snow and a catty yowl.

Teeth clacking in fear, Albie raced along the river bank and splashed into the shallows to throw off his scent. The cold stole his breath but he pushed on deeper into the elms, ash and poplars where the snow was thin on the ground. Albie spotted a natural alcove formed by a fallen willow and hauled himself into it. He shivered in the darkness, listening.

Minutes passed in an eerie silence. Then it began. A rhythmic splintering of twigs, *crunch, crunch, crunch*, as giant footsteps drew close. Beyond the stripped, spidery fronds of the tree, a deep exhalation, then a snort. A blur of brown fur swished past the opening of Albie's hiding place. Strange, intoxicating odours wafted into Albie's gaping nostrils. With another snort, a bear's nose poked through the branches.

'Come,' it said in a soft female voice, then withdrew.

Oh boy, oh boy, oh boy. Unable to control himself at all, Albie ambled out under from the tree to see big brown buttocks swinging seductively from side to side. The bear turned and lifted its jaws to reveal a young woman's face, smeared with camouflage stripes. She looked him up and down, then pulled the bear's head back into place.

'Begin!' she said, her voice gruff suddenly.

Albie recoiled as the sabre-tooth tiger emerged from behind a tree, took position behind the bear and held aloft its wooden sword. Other shapes rustled in the undergrowth around. There was a splash at the water's edge and a long dark shape crawled on its belly up the bank towards them. Albie recognised the gnarled snout of a crocodile. It came to rest by the willow with a hiss, tail twitching.

'Incipio!' cried the tiger, swiping down with the sword.

The bear stepped towards Albie, swivelled, and up went her big, brown furry rear. Instinctively, he went to it, head low, sniffing. Wonderful perfumes of flower stamen and fish blood lured him closer. She circled and he followed. Round and round and round. Every time Albie drew near, she bounded forwards. The tease! He wanted to touch her so bad it was unbearable. He took bigger leaps, paws wide, scratching desperately at her back. Suddenly, her fur was snagged in his claws and, as she lurched, she dragged him with her.

'Mutatio!' cried the tiger.

Blood rising, sweet electricity coursing through his loins, Albie hauled himself onto her back, hind legs dragging on the ground. She struggled then sighed. He bit the folds of her neck and shuddered into her, once, twice, again and again. From the corner of his eye he saw the tiger pacing back and forth. With a grunt, he let go. The bear wriggled from beneath him and dashed into the undergrowth.

Albie crumpled, drained, stars dazzling in his eyes, strangely happy. The tiger circled him once, purring, then it was gone too. The crocodile pushed its snout into Albie's face. For a few seconds it breathed asthmatically, open jaws reeking of London Pride, then it turned and swished towards the river, leaving Albie alone in the falling snow.

*

Daylight woke Albie, encrusted in white by the fallen willow. He shook the snow from his back and went to the river to drink. The water numbed his tongue but it was good. He hungrily scanned the shallows for signs of fish. Nothing. Harrumph harrumph. Stupid fish.

Yawning, he ambled up the river bank onto the path. He would have to find food somewhere else. Home, perhaps. He struggled to picture it. All he could remember was a box beneath a bed. There was a holdall, too, somewhere. Where had he put that?

The playing fields were covered in a blanket of snow. A watery sun seeped through the clouds and dazzled the crystals on the trees. Albie recognised the tower-block looming far away. Home. He shambled through the trees around the old river but the going was slow. Shouts and calls drifted on the wind – humans, up and about. Humans who wouldn't understand what he was doing out here, looking like this. Panicking now, Albie bounded across open land, bursts of white powder exploding at his feet, and crashed into the woodland by the Lee Navigation.

It was even noisier here. The thud of snowballs and children's laughter. Someone was tramping through the undergrowth towards him. Clump, clump, clump. And something else – the scent of a wolf. Albie dashed for cover in a cluster of shrubs on the marsh's edge and peered out at a woman with an Alsatian on a lead passing by. The dog strained to reach Albie, slobbering with excitement.

'Leave it!' yelped the woman, jerking the dog back to her side. 'What's wrong with you?'

Once they were out of sight, Albie moved from behind the shrub. There was a sharp gasp. He turned to see a small human boy in a woollen scarf and hat, clutching a snowball, mouth wide open. In the near distance were his three friends, motionless, staring. The boy dropped his snowball and screamed.

No! Albie cried, frantically waving his paws, *I'm not a bear!* But all that came from his mouth was a growl. The boy screamed again and fled towards the towpath, his companions stumbling after.

No, no, no! Albie sat on his haunches and put his paws to his head. Stupid, stupid, stupid. He could hear the boys' cries echo across the playing fields. Everything was ruined. By now they'd be crossing the bridge to their Mums and Dads. They'd tell on him for sure. Fulcher would find out. There'd be a right old hoo-ha. A really big stink.

Albie scrabbled for the shoelace ties on his suit but couldn't find them. Where was the join? The furs were wrapped seamlessly all around. He tried tearing off the arms but his claws drew blood. The fur was soft over flesh. No sign of coat hanger wires or stitching. Same went for his headpiece. Albie could feel only a muzzle. His eyes stared out through a forest of brown fur. He wrenched at his suit until he was in pain all over. Sobbing tearlessly, he ran through the trees towards the footbridge to Sudbury Court. *Home time for Albie*, Mammy used to say when she collected him from the school gates, bruised from the kicking and punching. *Home time for Albie*.

When he neared the bridge he saw a group of men coming in the opposite direction. One held a garden fork. Another clutched a pair of binoculars. They were pointing at the marsh. Their faces looked mean and serious. Albie fled in the direction he had come, running back across the playing fields towards the old river. In the woods he found an old tarpaulin and crawled beneath.

Perhaps they wouldn't come this far. Perhaps they didn't really believe the boys' story. They were just being Daddies, all manly and suspicious. Nobody believes what little kids say. Nobody believed him when he found the bear paw all those years ago. They laughed. They told him his Daddy died of embarrassment because his only son was an idiot.

Poxy Moxley
Found a bear but it was only a foxy
And that was the end of fatty, spotty, poxy Moxley

A helicopter chugga-chugga-chugged overhead, blowing mini blizzards of snow from the tree tops. Albie peered across the marsh. Policemen amassed by the changing rooms. Men with rifles fanned out across the football pitches. Others stalked the woodland, beating the undergrowth with sticks. Tarpaulin was no good to him now, no good at all. They would find him for sure. His only escape was across the river.

Swirls of mist rose from the water. He could just make out the black poplars on the other side, tilted like tombstones. Albie splashed in. The sodden furs pulled him down but he could feel the riverbed beneath his paws. He powered across in a few strides and shook himself clear. The bank was steep and hard to grip. As he reached the top another helicopter emerged from over Leyton, forcing him to the water's edge again, shaking with exhaustion.

Trapped.

Then he heard it. A muted horn through the mist. It blew once, then twice, then a third time – really close, like it was inside his ears. A red narrowboat pushed through the mist, covered in pictures of roses, hovering above the shallows on a cloud of steam, doves flapping all around. A lady at the prow clutched a pole with a noose on it. The boat angled towards the river bank where Albie cowered in utter confusion.

'There, there,' said the lady, stretching out the pole. She looked a bit like Mammy. 'You'll be alright.'

The noose looped over his head and tugged gently round his throat. Albie was drawn alongside the boat and up onto a fallen tree trunk until he was level with the prow.

'Come on!' the lady urged. 'You can do it, Mr Moxely. Now Jump!'

Albie jumped.

*

There was a tiny monkey on the lady's shoulder. It squeaked merrily at Albie as she led him along the roof of the narrowboat and down into the stern. The riverbank disappeared behind a cloud of mist, dense as silk. All the trees were gone. No helicopters chugga-chugga-chugged. No shouts, no calls. Albie felt a wash of relief, like all the badness in his life had floated away on a cloud. There was nothing left but the boat and the kind lady holding out a funny hat. He tried to take it but his big paws could only bat it from side to side.

'Never mind, Mr Moxely. I'll do it for you.'

The lady placed the hat on his head. 'Welcome to the Unmoored Manor of Mutating Manifestation,' she said. 'You have officially left British soil. The only law you need obey is the law of UMMM. And our only law is that your own will is the law. And so be it.'

Albie didn't understand any of that. It was all just *blah blah blah*. But he could smell something hot and meaty cooking beneath deck. His tummy growled. The lady drew back the curtain and gestured kindly for him to go inside. After what had been a most unusual Christmas, Albie Moxley was finally ready to have his dinner.

XVI

The Rabbit Hole

I met my own ghost down a rabbit hole behind Walthamstow
Marsh. I didn't expect to find it there. I was on my usual route
with Hendrix, cutting away towards the north eastern corner of
the marsh, where the railway passes over Coppermill Stream. The
bridge is so low that a triangle sign warns 5'0" and a neighbouring
triangle translates this into metric: 1.5 metres. All bases covered.
Even so, the ironwork must bear the DNA of a thousand bloodied
foreheads.

I call this bridge the Rabbit Hole. As in Alice's adventure, this
Rabbit Hole demands you shrink yourself. Some cyclists obey
the sign which tells them to disembark, leading their vehicles
like nervous ponies, while others double forward over their
handlebars. Tall people stoop at the waist, or bend their knees and
do 'The Groucho Marx'. Some crouch and run, as if disembarking
from a helicopter. Shorter folk like me bow our necks or crank our
heads. Once I saw a man limbo dance beneath the bridge. When
he came upright he showed no embarrassment, as if he'd picked
the most obvious way to pass through.

I entered the rabbit hole. Sunlight streaked through the gap between the two railway lines, creating a luminescent membrane through which I had to pass, as if entering the kingdom of God or the doorway of a Spielbergian spaceship. I stopped and pushed my head up between the tracks. At that moment a train came hurtling en-route to Stratford. Blinded by light and subsumed in the roar, I lost my footing on the ground beneath and fell through a hole in time to a childhood moment in Glossop, a town just outside Manchester.

We lived in a 1960s terrace house next to a disused field which backed onto a railway line. At night the clatter of trains serenaded me to sleep. By day the railway marked the threshold of a forbidden land. On the other side a tall white chimney, like a space rocket, dominated a series of industrial yards. Stories abounded of decapitated dogs and feral teen gangs lurking in the sidings. The two low, arched railway bridges on the far side of the field were the furthest points my brother and I were permitted to go. One led to a junkyard, a lawless zone where we could salvage ramps for our bike jumps. The other was at the end of a dense hedgerow behind a wire fence. We lifted the fence in three locations down its length, creating entrances wide enough for ten year-olds to wriggle through, and eke out adventures among the branches, concealed from pedestrians on the path. We named these entrances Tom, Dick and Harry, the tunnels in the 'great escape' from Stalag Luft III in 1943, in which my Great Uncle Ken had been a digger. When trains came along we'd run beneath the railway arch, waiting in a huddle for our ears to fill with thunder.

As I grew older, the bridge lost its innocent pleasures. One night my friend Alun was walking beneath the bridge when a man sprang from the shadows and grabbed him. Alun, fourteen years old, kicked his shin with his winkle-picker boots, tore away from his grasp and ran to my house in fright. The incident tipped reality sideways and from that point on I was more fascinated by what lurked within the shadows than what rumbled above.

That bridge in Glossop and this bridge in Walthamstow Marsh – they were suddenly one and the same. Stooped there, blasted by noise, I felt like Gulliver in Lilliput, travelling through the miniaturised landscape of my childhood. I could see a boy in the white light of the moment, a boy who no longer existed, who had long since been replaced by me. The boy was wide-eyed and smiling, unaware that I – a sinister 39 year old man – was watching on. It struck me. Perhaps that was who tried to grab Alun in 1987. His older self, a phantom in the shadows, unable to resist making contact.

Eventually the train passed and I was left with only the solemn arpeggios of the pigeons roosting above the adjacent stream.

I staggered from the bridge to face a dizzying panoply of features; winding country road; car park; railway siding with concrete sleepers; pylon; wedge of meadow; water tanks; the tower of a copper mill and gleaming oxygen cylinders. Fragments from a dream. Stuck out in the scrub by the reservoir fence was the giant banquet table they'd erected the year previously. I'd never seen anyone eating at this table, though I once saw a woman lying on it while a man photographed her. I'm not surprised. For me, eating here directly beneath the pylon cables would be like licking soup off a nuclear missile.

I sat on the chair at the head of the table, my legs dangling. In the bridge I'd been gigantic. Now I felt miniaturised. The pylon behind me was poised to stride over my head, lashing the sky with black cable. A passing freight train hooted 'Whoooooooooo'. Distorted `80s pop music seeped from a parked car. From the trees near the train track I could hear the laughter of kids blending with the banter of railway workmen until it sounded like they were all playing some sinister game together behind the weeping willow's shroud. I remembered how I used to spend endless afternoons in trees like those, private dens with leafy curtains in which we were free to dream up visions of secret spy rings, space stations and war bunkers.

Suddenly I understood what it was I loved about the marshland. Even though I had not grown up here, I'd known this place all my life. Squeezing into its thickets, stooping beneath its bridges, thrilling at the roar of trains, my childhood imagination had been released after decades of repression. No other landscape – no park, mountain, lake or coastline I have visited anywhere in the world – has such power to evoke that lost world of youth, when there was magic and terror to be found in the hedgerows, reservoirs and scrapheaps at the edge of town.

XVII

Behind the Spectacle

If you've ever wondered what operates the scenery of London's grand theatre, come to the little bridge at the top of Walthamstow Marsh. Here is where you can sneak backstage for a tour of its inner workings.

To the northwest of the marshland is a sprawl of reservoirs, pylons, flood channels, gas cylinders, warehouses and electricity exchanges – an uneasy alliance of electricity and water, where danger lurks behind every fence. These threats are narrated by a succession of imperious warning signs, beginning at the five foot bridge which leads away from the marsh, where a red rectangle reads: **Stop, Look, Listen, Beware of Trains.**

Another sign explains the load gauge for the high voltage power lines overhead, festooned with discs, wire loops and orange balls, like promenade lights in a British seaside town. These messages demand you pay heed to the grizzly fates that may await you. Crushed, electrocuted, severed, slashed, eviscerated, decapitated – beware! If you absolutely must pass through here, say the sign gods, at least know what you're getting into.

Coppermill Lane on the other side of the bridge is a fly-tipping hotspot where you can find piles of smashed cupboards, clothes and headless children's dolls. Set back in the road is a caged electricity exchange so lethal they have encased it in a second cage. A **Danger of Death** sign on the outer cage telescopes to another **Danger of Death** sign within, giving you double danger vision: **Warning! Watch out for warning signs!**

Running alongside the lane is Coppermill Stream. A long time ago it was alive with carp, perch, eels, chub, roach, pike, and fast-flowing enough to turn the wheel in the old Coppermill. These days its stagnant green surface is encrusted with Styrofoam cups, broken masonry and mouldering branches.

This mill the stream once served has a multifarious history. In the 14th century it was a corn mill. From the 17th Century it made gunpowder, then paper, then leather, then linseed oil. In 1805 they began rolling copper ingots from smelted ore brought by boat from South Wales. The East London Waterworks Company bought the mill in 1860 and transformed it into a pumping station. The Romanesque tower which houses the Cornish Bull engine still looms over ramshackle prefabs, traffic cones and a wooden jib. Today the site is a storage facility for Thames Water, who have plastered its gates with stark warnings:

Keep Out!

DANGER:
keep clear of water company structures and equipment

DANGER: Deep Water

The deep water of which they warn is in a reservoir containing two sandy islands. The first is barren but for a handful of trees topped with nests in which cormorants stretch their reptilian necks and fan their wings. The second is denser with trees, its outer edge ringed by concave gaps where chunks of earth have slid into the reservoir. God knows what lies on the ground within, possibly the bloodied corpse of the scientist who created this experiment, for no human can return to salvage his body. Fleets of cormorants bob in the water. Dozens more circle the canopy, gargling like gulls with throat cancer. A spray of faeces beneath their roosts is snowy white against the orange sand. This is a cormorant's world now.

Opposite the islands are the Coppermill Water Treatment Works, which assumed the role of the defunct Middlesex filter beds after 1969. Behind mesh fencing, networks of pipes criss-cross pools, overlooked by floodlights and two skeletal towers which rise on either side of a sand pyramid. This landscape stretches as far as the eye can see, all the way to Anish Kapoor's Orbit Tower in Stratford, as if East London is a vast filter system presided over by twisted robot overlords.

As Coppermill Lane approaches Walthamstow, houses appear among the caged electricity exchanges and fencing. Then you see it, coiling between the waterworks and the Victorian terraces: the Lee Flood Relief Channel, a majestic slab of concrete with uniform sloped sides. There are no fish in its shallows or life on its carefully mown edges. A swan cruising the channel seems confused and disappointed, like someone on a stage set absent-mindedly turning on the kitchen tap. The maintenance access gates are cluttered with warnings:

No Parking

No Unauthorised Persons

No Entry

Danger: Deep Water!

Danger of injury and of drowning

This pathologically pessimistic narrative pushes the casual walker away. *Go back to the houses and pubs of Walthamstow, there is nothing for you here.* You're forced through silent streets towards a railway bridge fenced off with yet more signs: **NO DUMPING. NO BALL GAMES. NO ENTRY.** In this place behind the spectacle, unseen municipal entities shout their bylaws in BLOCK CAPS. Their signs feel like emergency messages broadcasting after an apocalypse. The only literature in a post-human world.

But some humans remain, if you care to look. A band of survivors are trying to keep alive the memory of what this place did for Britain in its heyday. They are led by Lindsay Collier from the Pump House Museum, which stands on the site of the Low Manor sewerage works, now known unceremoniously as the South Access Road.

The museum's tumbledown yard contains locally-built transportation, including a 1940s Victoria line tube train on bricks, a Routemaster bus and a rusty German tram. Within the pump house is an Edwardian tool shop, where a man restores old engine parts. Lindsay's ambition is to excavate the history of the Lower Lea, bring back those local artefacts – Roe's triplane, for instance – which were sent away to museums across Britain, and trace the route of unsung industrial pioneers through a topography which has since been overlaid with property developments, leisure

facilities and distribution warehouses.

He will enthusiastically regale a visitor with facts about British firsts. The first electrified tram. The first bus. The first balloon flight. The first monorail. The first British car powered by an internal combustion engine, built by Frederic Bremer in 1894. The first British aeroplane flight. The Lotus Car Company, started in Tottenham in 1953 by Colin Chapman. Mosquito aeroplanes built at the Wrightons Furniture factory in Walthamstow. Sir Alan Cobham's in-flight refuelling system and aviation displays at Low Hall. Sir Joseph Swan's invention of the light bulb, twenty years before Edison. The first diode, invented by Ambrose Fleming at Ponder's End in 1904. Dazzling railway innovations in Leyton. Ship-building feats at Leamouth. All of this was created in the Lower Lea Valley.

Lindsay and his helpers are like unpaid archivists working in the basement of a giant corporate skyscraper, piecing together fragments from musty old files and film reels, looking for London's lost narrative. Their motivation is not money, but an opportunity to resurrect their local story and tell it to the world. It seems unlikely that such a feat is being attempted on the desolate South Access Road, where their neighbours are domed brick warehouses and yards piled with steel pipes, traffic cones and plastic fencing. But this is a place where the old ways persist, despite the near-obliteration of the rural landscape.

Not far from the Pump House is a trail known as The Black Path. For hundreds of years The Black Path has been a route from Walthamstow to Hackney and the big city beyond. Before a bridge was built over the Lea in 1758, a foot ferry was the only way to cross the river. After the bridge was built people cut across the marsh by foot or by horse, possibly to avoid tolls on the Lea Bridge Turnpike, taking their wares to Mare Street, London

Fields, Columbia Road and, finally, Smithfield. The path became known as the Market Porter's Route or the 'Porter's Way'. Why the nickname 'The Black Path' stuck is less certain.

The land around the path was once the location of Low Hall Manor House, built in 1344. After the 17th Century it was replaced with a farmhouse which existed until 1944 when it was obliterated by a V1 rocket. In the 1870s the Low Hall Manor House grounds became sewerage works, for which Lindsay's beloved pump house was built. A tramline running adjacent to the Black Path connected this sewerage plant to the railway. Some historians speculate that it was the ash from the tram which fell on the route gave the path its name.

What began as a Georgian desire path has persisted through the centuries in a landscape that has transformed entirely from rural to industrial. The path zig-zags improbably within a network of industrial estates, passing through TRS International Foods, Allied Bakeries, distribution warehouses, fleets of trucks and dry cleaning depots. Ventilation fans whir and hydraulic fork-lifts whinny. Workers chatter on their cigarette breaks. Radios blare. A stench of diesel, baked bread and turpentine fills the air. In between warehouses, ditches are piled with discarded trolleys, containers and oil drums. Every wall is plastered with warnings:

Dogs patrol the premises.

CCTV is in operation at all times.

This site is alarmed.

No unauthorised admittance.

It's extraordinary that The Black Path has not been subsumed by industry. It is like a grease stain on a piece of paper, upon which no ink will settle. It repels all progress. It endures even fire.

On the 24th May 2004, a blaze began in a warehouse on Argall Avenue, on The Black Path's route. Inside were over a hundred works of contemporary British art from Charles Saatchi's collection, one of which was the Chapman Brothers' *Hell*. The brothers' diorama of Nazi soldiers committing brutal atrocities and deviant sexual acts melted in the inferno. Not even Hell could withstand history's curse. Art critic Jonathan Jones wrote of *Hell*'s destruction: 'The setting seems singularly appropriate for its Viking send-off. Leyton is part of the post-apocalyptic east London landscape this art always mythologised.'

From Argall Avenue The Black Path leads to the Argall Footbridge, a gauntlet of graffiti with high sides, topped with mesh wire to prevent people hurling themselves onto the railway below. Once on the other side, the path turns right along a graffiti-coated wall, crested with a row of broken champagne bottles to repel intruders from a yard piled with car parts. Someone has written on this wall in large black letters: **London Town!!** It welcomes you back as if you've just crossed a border. And in a sense, you have. The railway lines built in the 19th Century, much to the dismay of the commoners at the time, had an unintended conservational effect. They separated the inner marsh from the outer areas, protecting its meadows from Leyton and Walthamstow's future spread.

When you're safely on the marsh among the sullen horses, you can look back at those industrial estates and see a fate narrowly avoided. But for the railway, the marshland could have easily become incorporated into the engine room of London's spectacle. Other than The Black Path and the pump house, little of antiquity has survived on the other side of the Argall footbridge. Amidst the clutter of warehouses, gas cylinders and steaming chimneys, a solitary Victorian church spire pokes the horizon, like the outstretched hand of a drowning man.

XVIII

The Fires of London

Yes, sir, you can call me Iriz, because that's my name and it's been that way for forty-five years. I won't tell you what I am doing on my hands and knees, sucking the stamen from this Büyü plant on Walthamstow Marsh, because that will take a whole story. Although, if you must insist . . . and seeing as though there's nobody down here on the marsh but myself and a few other Büyü addicts who are making absolutely no sense whatsoever . . . I suppose I can give you the quick version if you let me have a final suck on this. Wow, this one's strong. *Lezzetli!*

Okay. So it all began with the fires of London. They started out somewhere near the M25. Buildings going up in flames for no apparent reason – disused warehouses in the beginning, then it spread to retail parks, office blocks and shopping centres. At first all you could see was smoke in the far distance, like clouds before a storm. I would gaze out with worry at the sky from the flat above my restaurant in Upper Clapton. Yes, a restaurant – Café Iriz, if you must know, best Turkish in Hackney but then I've never been a humble man and I sacrificed my marriage in the pursuit of this culinary dream. It seems odd to you now that I'm clad in a swan-feather loin cloth and streaked with mud. Maybe I'm even gibbering nonsense and you're only humouring me before you rob and kill me. That may be - Allah will suffice me - but please understand that almost everybody had a restaurant at that time. Hackney was a parade of gastropubs, Ocakbasi restaurants, Chicken Cottages, noodle bars, organic bakeries, gourmet pizzerias and curry houses. You name it, you could eat it. The closer the fires came, the more restaurants opened. It got so that the restaurants' main source of customers were other restaurateurs taking lunch breaks in each other's restaurants. We all ignored the fires and especially the news, which was bad for business. Instead the TVs in our restaurants showed cookery programmes on a permanent loop.

It was harder to ignore the fires when Stratford went up like a mangal, smoke billowing across the marsh, stinky from all that buried industrial waste. It really put customers off their kebabs. My neighbour Collin, head chef of the fairly reasonable (if a little under-spiced) Clapton Jerk House, would come and watch the fires with me from the top of Springfield Park. We saw flames rise from the Argall Trading Estate behind the marsh, spread across the Lea Bridge Road, engulfing the brand new Leyton Marsh Mega Rink ice skating centre. Collin shook his head and muttered something about it being a bad ting, but I was cheered by a surge in customers panic-buying tabule and börek. *Eat up! Eat up!* I said, *for tomorrow may never come.* And they laughed at that. There was real spirit back then, for a while.

After the fires died out on the marsh side of the Lea, they began cropping up in Homerton, Tottenham and Hackney Wick. It was all too close to home now. People got spooked. Oh yes, sir, as they say, 'If you can't stand the heat, get out of the kitchen', which is exactly what happened. There was a mass exodus to Tech City! Maybe you're from there? You seem too well-heeled to be a marsh dweller and your fingernails are clean. You say that you were transported here on some kind of narrowboat? How bizarre. Well, anyway. For years they'd been putting up barricades around that area of Shoreditch, Islington and Hackney where all the rich folk lived. As the fires got closer they erected a steel wall with surveillance cameras and snipers. It stretched the length of Kingsland Road and Mare Street, right down to the Thames. To enter you needed passes and suchlike. Some people got in. Others didn't. So it goes in life. We restaurateurs didn't even try. As mobs ran wild on our streets, looting shops and setting off more fires, we stood outside united – Turks, Caribbeans, Nigerians, Indians, Pakistanis – brandishing cricket bats and crowbars. Ha ha! You don't mess with restaurateurs. Well, you didn't in those days anyway.

Now you tell me, sir, what is a smart man like me to do with a dwindling customer base and even the restaurateurs sticking to their own places for defensive purposes? I see that you shake your head. Well, I'll tell you what you do, free of charge. You innovate, my friend. It was my entrepreneurial hunch that what Clapton needed was a restaurant serving locally foraged food. I know, I know, but if you want to make money in this business you have to listen to the people *with* the money, and what was left of the middle classes outside Tech City were obsessed with fresh ingredients, tearfully so, often breaking down in sobs at the sight of parsley. But with truck deliveries stopped because of the fires, my larders began to empty. I had no choice but to go foraging on the marshes. I wasn't entirely sure what I was doing so I encountered some bitter tastes, I can tell you, like licking cat piss! But I found Mugwort, mallow, spear thistle, blackberries, elderberries, cobnuts, acorns and nettles. These all went nicely into salads I prepared myself – wonderful with some grilled squirrel or rat beyti. I enticed a few locals to come and to taste my new delights. They were a bedraggled and inconsistent lot, not quite the standard of Hackney's golden years, but beggars cannot be choosers and by that time I was devouring my own dishes as desperately as they, eating up my meagre profits. Poor practice indeed, but what else could I do?

My foraging was limited by great expanses of the marsh being burned out, especially near the railways, bridges and roads. But one day I noticed something remarkable growing from the most charred areas. A purple-stemmed plant with yellow flowers and a long emerald stamen, shaped like a calf's tongue. The flowers were tasteless but the stamen, wow, it was honey sweet. As soon as I put it to my tongue I was lifted bodily upwards, as if to heaven! I couldn't resist forcing more into my mouth, letting it dissolve and burst those sweet flavours. Yes, sir, you're looking at this Büyü plant right here before me, and you are right, it is one and the same. I named it myself only moments after eating it for the first time, when the visions began. It came on so quick, like you wouldn't believe – if you can believe anything I say, sir, so confounded you seem. But I tell you, I saw hundreds of cows and horses in a procession across Walthamstow Marsh, men and women with fiery hair driving them, chanting, '*Let the voice of reason rise above this loony tide, this is the land of the people!*' Behind them sailed a fleet of Viking ships, bobbing and tilting as if the grass were an ocean. I was amazed by the sight of a crocodile, ridden by a goose in a top hat, twirling above the pylons like a Chinese dragon. Sweet lullabies sung by children drifted from the blackberry bushes and I followed the sound, desperate to find them, tears in my eyes, a strange joy in my heart. The songs led me to a clearing in the trees behind the railway line where I could hear electronic drums pounding, louder and louder, I could not for the life of me tell whether they were inside my head or without it, but what matter was that? I began to dance like I have never danced before, laughing and weeping at the same time.

Ah, I know, you think me mad. I wonder about that too. I have no idea how long I was on the marshes. It might have been days, or weeks, it's impossible to say, for there is nobody familiar left to ask. All I know is that I woke one morning, bearded and bedraggled, with an urge to go home. I staggered across the Lea Bridge, shocked to see flames rising from Clapton, heat shimmering the air, smoke so thick it was hard to see. There was great despair in my heart for I knew then what I would find – my beloved restaurant, a smouldering ruin. Oh, lamentable day! What savages! I shouted for Collin but there was no sign of him, only a charred shell where his Jerk House used to be. People of all ages were running through the streets, smashing windows and letting off fireworks. A man ran past me with flames bursting from his back. Can you imagine? It could have been me next, for without my fellow restaurateurs by my side I was nothing. Terrified for my life I ran back to the marshes, plunging through the rushes until I found a patch of my beloved Büyü. So beautiful it looked among the black ash that I fell upon it and sucked hard until there was a mighty roaring in my ears, followed by a most blissful peace, as if the city had been muted. Merrily I sat by the rushes and looked out at the fires of London burning, my ears brimming with sweet birdsong, butterflies dancing at my toes, and I wondered at the shapes the flames made against the dusk sky.

Ha ha! Yes, I know, that's me getting poetic and you think what funny nonsense from an old restaurateur, but I beg you not to judge me harshly. It's not a bad life out here. You can live happy and free, as long as you can stay away from the fighting dogs which roam the lands. Come under this railway arch to my sanctuary, where I have begun painting my visions onto the walls. See there, the bear that comes snuffling through the scrub during the crepuscular hours. See here, a crowd of old-century people angrily tearing down a fence. You said earlier that you were transported here on a narrowboat? Does it look like this red vessel painted here, which floats over the river in a cloud of doves? Ah, I see you begin to tremble. Don't panic, I have a cure for your fear. You've been patient, sir, while I tell my story, and it's clear you mean me no harm. I will give you some of my Büyü to eat. There you go. Suck on the nectar. Good, eh, sir? It's really the best way to appreciate all this broken beauty. Don't you think?

XIX

Endgames

The day Parliament stole time, things began to go wrong on the marshes.

Until the 1750s, the commoners of Hackney, Walthamstow and Leyton had shared the Lammas Lands of the Lower Lea. All parishioners had the right to graze their cattle on the lands from Lammas Day on the 1st August to the 25th of March, known as Lady Day, which was New Year's Day in the old calendar.

Then in 1751 an Act of Parliament decreed that Britain should switch to the Gregorian Calendar. In the new Calendar the New Year would begin on the 1st January instead of Lady Day. This meant that the 31st of December 1751 was followed by the 1st of January 1752, which seems perfectly natural to us, but must have mangled the poor brains of the agrarian populace. To facilitate the changeover, eleven days were removed from September 1752, so that the 2nd of September was followed by the 14th of September. At the orders of the government, twelve days simply disappeared.

There were a few snags, though, which had to be ironed out. Taxes were traditionally paid on Lady Day, but now that twelve days had vanished, rate payers faced paying for a week and a half that hadn't existed. To resolve this, the government pushed the payment date back by twelve days, so taxes were now due on April the 6th, which is where the beginning of the tax year remains, a Roman Road traversing our modern business calendar.

This hole in time created a rift between the parishes of Walthamstow and Leyton. While Leyton continued to bring the cattle for grazing on 1 August which was the Gregorian New Lammas Day, Walthamstow stuck to the Old Julian Lammas Day, which was now the 13th August. Cracks began to show. The progressive Leyton parishioners had to remove their cattle eleven days before the stubborn Walthamstow folk. There was now rivalry over an area of land which was becoming an increasingly valuable asset. Problems were exacerbated by The Walthamstow Slip, a skinny strip of land stretching from Eagle Pond, through Leyton Green, across the marshes to the Lea. This island territory of Walthamstow, adrift in the middle of Leyton, was separated from its home parish boundary by half a mile. Some local historians suggest this phenomenon occurred after a dead body was found by the Lea. When Leyton parishioners refused to bury it, Walthamstow's parishioners carried the corpse across the marshes. Ancient custom awarded ownership of the land to those who walked a dead body over it, and so their route became Walthamstow property. This strip was valuable land with high rates of income. Tensions rose. When locals went beating the boundaries in their annual ritual, scuffles broke out between the two parishes.

First, a slip in time. Then a slip in Walthamstow. But this was only the beginning of the land disputes. The Lower Lea had become the engine room of a global industrial revolution. Railways needed to cross the marshes. A rapidly expanding East London populace wanted clean water from the river. The Navigation required locks, docks and pubs for refreshment. What had been a rural backwater was now a glittering prize for water and rail companies, and they were prepared to dig deep into their pockets to get it. In 1838 the Northern and Eastern railway company bought an area of marsh from the commoners in return for money to pay their parish's share of building the union workhouse. In a meeting at the Ferry Boat Inn in 1854, The Lammas Lands Committee and The East London Waterworks negotiated the sale of another 17 acres of Walthamstow and Leyton Marshes in return for investment in the Leyton and Leytonstone national schools. This happened twice again in the 1860s and 1870s. Slowly, but surely, the rail and water companies crept onto the marshland.

The trouble with the Lammas Land Committee's strategy of giving up land for rewards was that the Waterworks Company assumed there was no barrier to their progress. Hurl a bag of money at the locals and they'd let you do whatever you wanted. Why bother with this merry dance of negotiation at all? If the locals refused they'd simply force them to sell. In 1890, without permission, the East London Waterworks Company began laying tram rails to the filter beds, cutting through a bridle path, and fencing off the area which is occupied today by the Lee Valley Riding School.

The commoners began to realise the value of their open spaces, not in financial terms but for its importance to their wellbeing. The Lammas Lands were an oasis in the centre of industrial revolution, a place for recreation, a shortcut into London. Locals demanded the return of the land which had been unlawfully taken. When the East London Waterworks Company refused, the people took action. On a rainy Bank Holiday on Lammas Day, August 1st 1892 a crowd of around 3,000 people gathered at Marsh Lane, carrying sticks, umbrellas, crowbars, saws and sledgehammers. Local historian Katy Andrews describes reports of a white bearded man with a placard on a walking stick which read 'Land Shall Not Be Sold Forever', a quote from Leviticus. Local Councillor Musgrove made a speech cautioning against violence or vandalism, before he and Councillor Henry Humphries led the crowed to the high railing, which they dismantled before lifting the tram rails.

The furious water company initiated proceedings against the commoners but so enshrined in law were the local's rights, they could not bully their way to a victory. They withdrew their claims, paid the legal costs and offered £100 to repair and improve the bridleway. In return they got to keep their tram rails. It was a victory for the newly born Lammas Lands Defence Committee. Its leaders became local heroes and this plaque placed in Marsh Lane:

IN COMMEMORATION OF
LAMMAS DAY 1892
WHEN THE PEOPLE OF LEYTON
LED BY C.G.MUSGRAVE, H.HUMPHREYS AND
E.C.PITTAM
ASSERTED THE COMMONERS RIGHTS
AND SUCCESSFULLY RESISTED
THE ATTEMPTED ENCROACHMENT UPON THESE
LANDS

*

Over on Hackney Marsh, Eton Mission was pushing for a handover of land to the public. Eton College had come to the marshes in the 1880s after a visitation from the Virgin Mary to Eton College's Chapel, telling them to help the poor of East London. They wanted to establish sporting activities on the marshes, but their boys were regularly ordered off the land, their goal posts confiscated. Eton Mission's pressure paid off. In 1893 the London Open Spaces Act transferred control of the land, 'free of all its previous existing rights' to the London County Council. Hackney Marsh was given to people of Hackney for recreational use 'in perpetuity' in 1894. Eleven years later the grazing rights in the Lammas Lands of Leyton were bought under the same conditions.

It didn't take long for the London Country Council to dip their hands into the bounty. In 1937 they grabbed an area of marsh from Adley Street to Homerton bridge on the south western side of the Lee Navigation and built the Kingsmead Estate on it. Two years later, war broke out and the marshes became a site for anti-aircraft guns, bomb disposal and dumping rubble.

With the threat of invasion gone, Sir Patrick Abercrombie suggested in his Greater London Plan of 1944 that the Lee Valley become a regional park. But it wasn't until 1961 that the Mayor of Hackney, Alderman Lou Sherman invited what was then known as the Civic Trust to appraise the Valley and its resources. The result was a document which declared: 'it will be a playground for Londoners against the background of London. This background – power stations, gas works, factories, railways, houses and flats – must be accepted and acknowledged in the landscape theme.' The marshes were registered as Common Land under the Commons Registration Act of 1965. The Lee Valley Regional Park Authority was formed in 1967 to manage them.

Despite noble declarations of a place for all Londoners, a dirty deal had already been done when a bill was pushed through the House Of Lords in 1956, permitting the quarrying of gravel in the marshes. Understanding local sensitivities, this right was not exercised until an application in 1979 by The Lee Valley Regional

Park Authority itself. The area of Walthamstow Marsh between the railway and reservoirs, containing land untouched since the ice age, was to be dug up and turned into a lake for motorised water sports, including parking and facilities. Leyton Marsh would be quarried next, but afterwards turned back into a playing field.

An organisation called Save the Marshes struck back in a display of cool, measured intellect. John Nash and a team of specialists in botany, ornithology and entomology, including Mike Knowles, David Gibbins, Brian Wurzell and Harry Briton carried out an exhaustive survey of the area called 'Walthamstow Marshes: Our Countryside Under Threat', which listed the marsh's flora and fauna, including

sedge
reed swamp   ragged robbin
St John's Wort
Thistle   meadowsweet   comfrey
wild hops
adder's tongue fern
butterflies   dragonflies
damselflies   red underwing moths
teal   kingfishers   sandpiper
little ringed plover
Lapwing   greenshank   dunlin
Skylarks   redwings
tree sparrows   warblers   goldfinches
skylarks   snipe
herons   kestrels

All this existed just across the water from the timber yards, factories and estates of East London, open to all who wished to roam. Campaign Chairman Mike Knowles wrote: 'Walthamstow

Marshes has spiritual value. It ministers to people's need for peace, openness, freedom, wildness and space. These things can be taken away and destroyed, but they cannot be artificially created or laid on.'

Thanks to the survey, the Minerals Subcommittee of the Greater London Council refused the Lee Valley Park Authority permission to extract gravel. In 1985, Walthamstow Marsh was given the status 'Site of Special Scientific Interest' under section 28 of the Wildlife and Countryside Act. A line had been drawn in the sand. These lands were special. They were not up for sale. These were the people's lands. They were a legacy to be handed down to generations.

And that – so they thought – was the end of that.

*

In the cartoon Scooby-Doo, it's usually the threatened sale of a property, such as a fairground, zoo, mansion or school, which drives ordinary people – white middle-aged men in particular – to such extremes as dressing up like a Yeti and chasing meddlers through corridors. At the time of the quarrying threat a bear was sighted by four boys on the marshes. The next big threat of development emerged in 2005, when it was announced that the Olympics were coming to the lower Lea Valley. Weeks later, the crocodile made its goose-murdering debut. A conspiracy theorist might suggest some kind of Scooby Doo shenanigans, perhaps on the part of those wishing to drive out locals and take the marsh for their own, or those hoping to bring attention to the marshes in order to protect them.

Whatever the truth, the rules of the game changed in 2005. There would be no more protracted negotiations. The Olympics meant big money was about to flow into the city. All eyes would be on East London. Its international reputation was at stake. It was time for the vested interest of government, commerce, industry, the media and local authorities to band together. This time nothing would get in their way.

One of the first declarations from the Olympic Delivery Authority affected the Manor Garden allotments, which were situated on the proposed Olympic site. The allotments had been created in 1900 by Major Arthur Villiers, a philanthropic director of Barings, so that deprived community locals could grow vegetables. Despite an outcry from the Manor Garden users, these were to be demolished and relocated to common land on Marsh Lane. In protest, a crowd gathered on Sunday, 17th December 2005 to beat the boundaries. As in 1892, it was raining. TV crews and journalists mingled in the throng. A man who called himself Lawrence of Leyton rang a bell and yelled, 'Oh Yea Oh Yea, they're giving our land away!' The crowd sang:

'Sing a song of Open Space and sing it far and wide,
Sing of ancient Lammas rights and justice on our side.
Let the voice of reason rise above this loony tide,
This is the land of the people!'

The protest failed and the allotments were relocated in 2007. There followed a succession of compulsory purchase orders from the ODA on large tracts of common land. Arena Field, to the South of Wick Field, where local football cup finals were played, was taken for the Olympics to house a five-story media centre. The East Marsh was dug up and turned into a car park.

The tipping point came when it was proposed that a temporary basketball facility should be built on Leyton Marsh. The Lee Valley

Park Regional Authority had agreed a lease arrangement to use the marsh in July 2011, long before the public were told in mid-December 2011. Marsh users were given until 2nd January 2012 to object, a tiny window of two weeks, slap bang in the middle of Christmas. Despite the ODA's clever timing, 1,250 people signed a petition against the plans. Objectors claimed there was little evidence that alternative venues had been sought out. Still, local councillors pushed it through, insisting that the contractual obligations to restore the marsh to its original state would be honoured. This, despite clear evidence in the 1979 survey that it was not possible to dig up a longstanding natural area and replace it without destroying the habitats of plants and insects, and the birds which feed on them.

Within a few months the diggers rolled onto the marsh. The wheels of history turned. As in 1979, an activist group was formed, this time called Save Leyton Marsh. As well as protesting the abuse of greenbelt land, they called for compensation in the form of improved public basketball courts in Leyton and warned of dangers beneath the topsoil, including asbestos, lead and contaminated rubble from houses shattered during the Blitz. Seventy years of nature had contained these dirty secrets. Now men in hard hats were obliviously hacking away at the surface.

Despite assurances to the Waltham Forest Planning Committee that they were only going to dig 15cm deep, contractors dug half a metre down and piled the rubble high, exposed to wind and rain. On the 14th March they found a 1kg German bomb. The site was evacuated while bomb disposal experts were called to the scene, seventy-two years after Davies and his team came to the marshes with the bomb that almost destroyed St Paul's Cathedral.

Events in the marsh's history connected across time. Occupy activists, camped outside St Paul's Cathedral, set up a second camp on the hallowed meadow which had saved that same Cathedral in 1940. Local protestors gathered once again to reassert their rights as they had done in 1892. Speeches were made. Cheers drifted over the rushes and ditches. Pandora's Box had been opened. This was no longer a frontline between marsh users and corporate interests. This was a frontline of the wider Occupy War. If St Paul's was its Western Front, this was its North Africa. Kris O'Donnell, from Occupy London, said: 'We have issues with the way this land is being dealt with. It is green belt land. Our aim is to assist the residents in any way we can.'

When asphalt trucks began to roll through Sandy Path, an access road beside the Lee Valley Ice Centre, protestors lay in front of the wheels to block their way. The police met with the Lee Valley Regional Park Authority to discuss how to shift the camp. Few politicians were in vocal support, but Haggerston ward councillor Barry Buitekant said: 'I do not think the ODA should go ahead with building training courts on Metropolitan Open Land, which has the same status as greenbelt land. I don't understand why the ODA were unable to find a brownfield site. They had several years to do it. They didn't even try.'

The Lee Valley Regional Park applied for an injunction against people camping on the land, claiming they were contravening byelaws. In an audacious display of doublethink it announced: 'We always take action where we have knowledge of an unlawful use of our land and in this case we are keen to safeguard Leyton Marsh.'

The eviction notice was served. The ODA repeated the claim that they were obliged to return the site to its previous state by the 15th of October. A spokesperson added: 'After the temporary structure is dismantled, they will benefit from £65,000 of improvements to the area and its wildlife habitats, funded by the ODA.'

The protestors lost a High Court battle against the injunction. The game was up. Just after at 7.30am on the 10th of April bailiffs arrived at the site and began to remove tents, arresting six protestors. The trucks rolled in, churning Sandy Path into a bog of blood red mud.

To the South, more trouble was brewing near the A12 flyover by Wick Woodland. Contrary to stated plans, the ODA blocked off the towpath alongside the Olympic Park for twelfth-hour security reasons they were unwilling to divulge, forcing cyclists to veer up onto the dangerous dual carriageway. Protestors amassed there at the weekends with sandwiches and flasks of tea, facing down police. Bewildered troops freshly back from Afghanistan were made to sit beneath a tarpaulin and guard a section of London canal. Seventy years after the Blitz, militarisation had returned to the marshland. Anti-aircraft weaponry was trained on the skies from the roofs of residential tower blocks. Local protest was countered with the mantra of 'special circumstances'. The reputation of Britain and her corporate sponsors was at stake. The safety of the Games was more important than a bunch of scruffy locals whinging about walking their dogs, playing football, cycling to work and not having heat seeking weaponry installed on their roof.

Meanwhile, on Leyton Marsh, the basketball centre rose from the bulldozed earth, tall as an aircraft hangar, pristine, smooth and windowless. Two ribbed ventilation chimneys were bolted to the outside of back wall. Men in yellow jackets took up guard posts at each corner. Generators began to whirr. The Olympic beast was alive.

*

In 1752, twelve days were taken from the calendar, igniting trouble on the marshes as a newly divided community realised the value of their land. In 2012, the two weeks cordoned off for the Olympic Games sparked another catalytic shift in the marsh's fortunes. A hole was torn in the shield of common law, allowing corporate money into a public space which had been denied to vested interests for centuries. The building of temporary basketball courts altered the land usage, turning a greenfield site into a brownfield site 'suitable for purposes of assembly and leisure', making life much easier for future developers. It was a manoeuvre which the Victorian water and rail companies could never have dreamed possible.

But this doesn't mean that the idea of open, free, common land has been vanquished. Across the water, kestrels hover, butterflies dance and swans flock over cows, horses and wildflower meadows. People walk dogs, chop logs, smoke joints, fly kites, kiss in the bushes, photograph wildflowers, pick berries and jog through the woodland. In pubs across Clapton, Walthamstow, Leyton and Hackney Wick, marsh lovers plan their defence strategy, print T-shirts, write articles and lobby politicians. The same forces that rose in 1892 and 1979 to prevent the appropriation of this open space are at work today. They are the latest defenders of the marshes, and they are not going anywhere.

XX

The Battlefield

On a Saturday in June 2012, Hendrix and I walked across the battlefield of Leyton Marsh. Mounds of freshly dug earth were piled where the Olympic basketball practice courts were to be built. The tents of Occupy protestors lined the fencing, colourful ribbons fluttering from their tops, like the day before Agincourt. Reggae blared from stereos, the air sweet with campfire smoke. As I picked over the guy ropes, reading protest leaflets pinned to the fence, I understood how it must feel in a country where a foreign army has come to fight on behalf of the locals – grateful, but bewildered and a little suspicious.

'Do you know the marsh well?' asked a fresh-faced activist handing out leaflets. 'Do you know what's been happening here?'

Sullenly, I took his leaflet and stuffed it into my pocket without looking at it. Everywhere I looked, twentysomethings were in conversation with mildly bored police officers. A van full of alsatians was parked beyond the perimeter fence by the freshly dug strips of land. Workmen lingered, picking at their fingernails. A man with ginger dreadlocks poked at a fire and supped a can of lager. A bleary eyed girl poked her head from a tent, blinking in the late morning. I wished they would all go, the protestors, the workers, the police, the dogs, the fucking lot of them. I knew these were bad thoughts I was having, bad selfish thoughts, but this was a mass pitch invasion and I was sick of it. The city had spilled over the Lea. It encroached on every space. A permanent relay of Chinooks roared from Enfield toward the Olympic park. Omnipresent surveillance copters were black nails hammered into the sky. The noise was a permanent headache. The rumble of trucks and Lee Valley Authority vehicles. The sight of cranes. Hendrix in the grass around Leyton Marsh, sticking his nose into the Blitz toxins leaking from the churned meadow. It was too much.

I drifted away from the pamphleteer to a man by the fence wearing a luminous yellow jacket over a suit. A low ranking Olympic Delivery Authority official perhaps. There was something about his ruddy cheeks and short stature, something I recognised. I asked him how his day was going. 'Modestly well,' he replied, eyeing me suspiciously. I caught a glance of the laminated ID card hanging from his belt: **H. Hazlehurst**.

'Do you know a man called Octavius Whipple?' I asked. The blood drained from his face.

'It's okay,' I said softly, 'I know of your plight.'

Hazlehurst's eyes were paranoid, darting from left to right as he mumbled fragmented details of his sojourn in hospital under the Mental Health Act, where he'd been encouraged to write down the details of his time-travelling fantasy. He told me Whipple was living with a man named Lorenzo in a flat above a recording studio in Dalston. They had made some well-received limited edition LPs documenting Whipple's walks through modern London using Victorian maps, his words spoken over what Hazlehurst described as, 'Lorenzo's dreadful electrocuted music'. Whipple was quite the local hero and regular performer at Café Oto. I was keen to ask Hazlehurst more but we'd caught the eye of an ODA official who began to approach.

Hazlehurst paled. 'I must bid you good day, Sir.' He retreated though a gap in the fence. I didn't attempt to pursue him. I was aware of suspicious stares from both activists and officials, so I beat a retreat across the footbridge to Millfields Park. I decided to walk along the Navigation to Hackney Marsh and the Old River Lea, where I could indulge in the illusion I was exempt from the Olympic imperative.

The Navigation was sparklingly clean. Gone was the island of mulch beside the Weir. No swirls of oil. Even the footballs were gone. The canal cleaning boats had been out in force, dragging bottles, cans and styrofoam takeaway boxes onto their conveyor belts. A black speedboat like an aquatic BMW, helmed a man with a canary yellow jumper draped over his shoulders, zipped past. Regular narrowboats had been banned from the Navigation south of this point. The waterway was now the preserve of smart, clean vessels, permission slips stuck to their windows, their decks hung with bunting.

When I reached the Homerton bridge I instinctively glanced up at Matchmaker Wharf and caught the eye of a young man on the balcony of the seventh floor, smoking and biting his fingernails. A slim Indian girl appeared behind him, momentarily, but he ushered her back inside and continued to watch me. He seemed angry, maybe frightened. I could tell he was looking for something on the towpath. Was it me? I hurried away through the shrub towards the Hackney Marsh playing fields.

I'd only got ten yards when a woman in a yellow jacket stopped me. 'Access is restricted', she said. I peered over her shoulder to see a single fence, perhaps 100 metres long, a couple of trucks and a line of yellow tape strewn loosely on the ground round the perimeter. Otherwise the marsh was as normal. I knew they were preparing for BBC Radio 1's *Hackney Weekend*, a pre-Olympic festival to be held on the marsh, featuring Jessie J, Professor Green, Will.i.am, David Guetta and Leona Lewis. But that was weeks away. The original planning consent for the event had stated that 'large areas of the common will still be available to the public during these events for walking, relaxing and sporting activities'. The wild land by the Old River was not part of the festival plan, as far as I was aware.

Assuring the woman I would keep Hendrix on a lead and stick to the outside of the marsh, I made a beeline for the trees. I was quickly intercepted by a man on a bicycle in a high visibility jacket and a cycling helmet, which seemed an unnecessary precaution for riding on a football pitch.

'This is private property,' he panted.

'Sorry?' I stopped at this. It felt like the strangest, most surprising thing that anybody could possibly say.

'You're on private property,' he gestured at the yellow tape, much in the same way my four-year old daughter might say: 'This string is the door to my magic castle' and I, humouring her, might reply, 'Of course, my Princess!'

'But this is where I walk my dog,' I said. 'I'm going to the river.'

'You have to leave I'm afraid, you're on private property.' He began to incant some legalese about health and safety but I couldn't take it in. I gazed over his fat head at the tops of the stadia, the new tower blocks and the Orbit Tower. I imagined they were giant machines advancing on the marsh, piloted by the Neo Gods of Commerce, issuing their byelaws in Dalek voices through this deputy's cycle helmet.

I wish I could write that I made a bold protest there on the marsh that day. I wish I could say I pulled a clump of grass from the ground, sprinkled it over my head and declared, 'Well, if this marsh is private property, then I am now a piece of common land and you can't touch me.' But I didn't do anything. I dolefully retreated to the Navigation, passing the women who had spoken to me first. Her raised eyebrows said: *I told you so.*

I couldn't return to Hackney Marsh for another month. Instead of the fortnight pegged for the event, they restricted access to all areas for four weeks. At home on the evening of Saturday 23rd June, I switched on the TV to see Beyonce wearing wellies in the rain on Hackney Marsh, while Jay Z rapped on stage, and the soil cried under the feet of an invading force of 100,000 MOR pop fans on the borderland where Saxon armies once faced their Danish enemies. When the battle was done, the playing fields were torn and pitted with craters. The council had promised that the football pitches would be fully restored by the time the football season began in September, but by March 2013 ten of the pitches were unsuitable for play. Players going in for sliding tackles shredded their skin on embedded bottle tops. The cricket pitches, installed the previous year, were so damaged the season was called off entirely. Despite the carnage, the council proposed that further major public events could be held here. A lot more cash can be made from festivals than free sports grounds for local footballers and cricketers. Johnnie Walker, chairman of Hackney and Leyton Sunday Football League, asked, 'Where does legacy come in?'

'Let's face it,' the Neo-Gods answered through their yellow jacketed drone army: 'The Olympics are over. Let the endgames begin!'

*

When the Olympic circus left town, they took down the basketball centre on Leyton Marsh. I paused on the aqueduct path each day and watched them detach the ventilation shafts, tear off the wall panels and pile them up for the trucks to remove. There was no crowd to watch them this time. The building was dismantled in groggy silence. Observing this every day from the ridge of the old aqueduct was like watching a film in reverse. After the building materials were removed, there was nothing left but a rectangle of churned soil. Workmen gathered in a long line and rolled giant turf across the soil, as if covering a grave.

Within days this turf had become waterlogged. Glistening pools of stagnant water dotted the meadow. Despite assurances that the marsh would be restored, much of the original topsoil had been thrown away and new soil used to fill in the marsh. Twelve centimetres beneath the ground they had laid a geo-textile membrane to assist possible future excavation.

The following summer daisies, dandelions and buttercups sprang up on Leyton Marsh, everywhere except for that vast rectangle of wonky turf where the basketball courts had stood, a battlefield where no poppies could grow. Beside the meadow on Essex Wharf – that peninsula of unascribed waste ground which had startled me when I first came to Millfields Park in 2008 – work began on new development. Gas tanks, diggers and prefab huts were lined up by the barb wire fence. Barges loaded with rubbish sat low in the water by the rusting bulwarks. Men with hard hats sank corkscrew drills deep into the earth where the knacker's yard for dead horses had once oozed blood.

The basketball experiment had been only a first foray into the marshland. London's property developers had finally crossed the Lea. Now their cranes bristled along the length of the river like the helmets and pikes of a mediaeval army. A new battle line had been drawn.

XXI

Naja's Ark

At dusk two teenagers clamber from their nests in the roof of the ruined Leyton Marsh Mega Rink.

They descend the hard angles of girders, silhouetted against the red sky, gripping onto creepers. When they reach the ground, the tall girl leads with purposeful strides, a sack slung over her shoulder, parting the long grass for her companion to follow, a skinny boy with hair tendrils dangling over his shoulders. He tries to avert his gaze from the girl's majestic, swinging buttocks and listens out for bullmastiffs in the undergrowth, knuckles white around his spear.

They walk in silence by the Lea River, a syrup of black silt, motionless as an oil painting, bristling with car chassis, narrowboat wrecks and dead trees. Pustules on the surface cough wisps of green gas. Across the river is a landslide of demolished riverside apartment blocks, behind which rise the silver walls of Tech City, stretching for miles towards the Thames, lights twinkling.

Soon they reach the railway bridge, a twist of latticed iron, broken and bowed into the river like the spine of a brontosaurus.

Its only fully intact archway is concealed behind a dense thicket of briars. Naja pushes through a macheted slit she has lovingly maintained these past years, a vulva is how she thinks of it, a passageway to the womb of her soul. Inside she lays down her sack and begins to arrange its contents on the concrete, humming one of her dubs, 'Mmmmmmm, ghuhghuhghuh, mmm, guh, guh,', her throat pulsing like a frog's. When she's ready she removes her dog-skin boots, demurely arranges her feathered skirts, and sits cross-legged to wait for her punters.

The boy, Badru, pauses outside the entrance to hear Naja's dub. It's the sound of a thousand doves crying in an endless well which goes all the way down to the core of the earth and the eternal, raging fire. Oh man. Everything she does enflames him. Badru does a little hop-step dance, then continues under the bridge. He clambers onto a pile of bricks, the *dealing knoll*, and stands high above the grass, grinning at the sight of Walthy Marsh stretching before him, a golden blur of reeds rippling like liquid fire in the sunset. The tilted pylons on the horizon are beaded with carrion crows. Crickets chirrup. Midges swirl like black smoke from waterlogged ditches. Badru never tires of it, never. Despite everything there has been, and will be, there's always this.

Badru wishes he could stay on the knoll all evening and drink the sky, but there's work to be done. He goes down to the river's edge and conceals himself in the reeds. Watching across the water, there is movement at Robin Hood point. A woman on a raft. She stabs at the leathery surface scum with a stick, breaking it into loose scabs, then scrabbles to the back of the raft and gracelessly punts herself forward with a long pole.

As Badru watches, a boy with smoky olive skin, heavy eyebrows and a jutting jaw joins him, nervously fondling a necklace festooned with gull heads.

'Whereyuhbeen, Pegger?' Badru does his best to hide his anger. 'Been around,' says Pegger, petulantly waggling his jaw. 'Innt no business. How many?'

Badru squints. A second figure is clambering over the rim of rubble beyond Robin Hood point. 'Two, seems like.'

'Two?' Pegger spits a bolus of phlegm into the mud. 'Naja got us stuck on Walfy marsh dealing to a few punters for a couple o'coins. Down in Wick Wood they make them city fuckers pay heavy gold.'

'Wick Woodlanders are bandits.'

'This innt no good anymore,' says Peger. ''Naja's got her face deep in the merch. Does shit to yer brain.'

Badru shakes his head. There's nothing wrong with Naja's brain. As for Pegger, he's not so sure these days. He disappears for days in the forests around Hackney Wick and Stratford, where gangs with dogs roam the stadia and battle for supremacy on Hackney Marsh. Legends say there are bears and crocodiles by the old river, and mysterious vessels, belching smoke, which steal people from time. It's no place for a boy who wants to live. When Pegger returns from his jaunts his eyes are always fierce and bloodshot, like you can see the nerves jangling in his brain, connecting up ideas that shouldn't be connected. Like he's hatching a plot.

The woman clambers off the raft into the scrub only metres away from the boys' hiding place. Badru doesn't recognise her. A first-timer, for sure. She seems confused about what to do, ambling back and forth, flinching at the sound of dog barks beyond the ridge of the old aqueduct. Tentatively, she begins to walk towards the railway bridge.

'Watch him,' Badru nods toward the man searching for a raft on the opposite bank. 'I'll take this 'un.'

*

Badru leads the punter to the archway. Naja sits bolt upright like a pharaoh in the gloom, bedecked in furs and feathers, the merch laid out before her: books, comics, pamphlets, magazines and wooden musical instruments. She cracks a glow stick. The arch fills with bright green light, illuminating the graffiti which covers every inch of brickwork. Intricately detailed herons, kestrels and kingfishers flock from a forest of cranes. A curly-horned cow is bifurcated by a digger's claw. Men holding mastiffs on chains chase screaming children. A crocodile swallows a goose. Crushed butterflies bleed beneath truck wheels. Bombs rain on a cathedral dome. A train belches smoke. Doves spiral from the back of an ornately decorated narrowboat, steered by a bear in a fedora hat. There are words and numbers too: **Lammas, Anonymous, Occupy, 1892, Whipple, Olympiad.** Many of these were painted long before Naja's time and much of what they depict no longer exists, except in their books.

The woman is in her forties, plump and hump-backed like most city dwellers. The punters often come across the Lea swathed in protective layers of black nylon and jackboots, but this one looks like she just got lost in her garden. Pointy pink shoes, spattered in mud, jut from beneath a floral plastic smock. She tells them in a cracked voice that her name is Heraldine. Badru guides her to the merch, where she flops down with a wheeze, then stands stiffly behind Naja's shoulder, spear raised.

'They said this place existed,' murmurs Heraldine, caressing the merch with trembling fingertips, 'but I didn't believe them.' She picks up a tattered hardback of *Treasure Island* and thrusts her face between its pages, inhaling deeply. *She's a sniffer*, notes Naja. For a sniffer the words aren't important. It's the feel of paper, the rasp of pages, the musty stink. Sometimes the touch of a book isn't enough. They want the harder stuff. They stagger onto the marsh and plunge their arms deep into the bog, rub mud over their faces, push it onto their mouths until they gag, their tongues wakened to malty microbes and salty clay, the flavour of wild earth, a trace memory of a childhood they have never experienced.

Heraldine opens another book and reads from the page, following the words with her forefinger as she speaks them. 'In every epoch man has thought himself at a turning point of history.' Naja smiles. *The Phenomenon of Man*. An old priest from hundreds of years ago who said that life was progressing towards a moment of perfect unity, when fragments would become the whole and everything – all people, even time itself – would one day converge on God. So sayeth the preacher man. Naja doesn't know. She has recurring dreams of water rising to swallow the world. The crows, with nowhere to land, grow weary and fall from the sky, one by one, until the air is empty and silent. What if we move towards God, thinks Naja, and it turns out that God does not want us?

Heraldine tosses the book down and picks up another, its dust jacket weathered like an old map. She rubs it against her cheek, thrilling at its roughness. In the city, nothing decays, nothing rots, everything is digitised, pristine and pure. She flicks through the gloriously stained pages until a fragment catches her eye. She reads: 'That deep romantic chasm which slanted down the green hill athwart a cedarn cover. A savage place! As holy and enchanted as e'er beneath a waning moon was haunted by woman wailing for her demon-lover!'

Wind whips through the entrance suddenly, blowing open the books and magazines. The sound of fluttering paper breaks Heraldine's heart. She begins to sob. Badru grips his spear tighter. An angry red evening seeps through the wall of briars. He thinks about Pegger out by the river alone, about how his eyes are so wild lately, and he worries.

*

With growing agitation, Pegger watches the man wobbling on the raft towards him. All that money and power and still they slip from the walls of their city to come here, crying their tiny hearts out, confessing their sins, dishing out coins for old paper, like nothing had happened these past hundred years.

Pegger stuffs a pinch of Büyü powder up his nose, letting the alkaloid toxins trickle down his throat, hoping it'll give him the strength to carry out what he intends to do, wondering whether Naja and Badru will forgive him. But a time comes when a boy must become a man. This whole dealing game was always Naja's thing, not his. When he was a little kid, Naja read adventures to him – Dick Turpin, Captain Nemo, Tarzan, Robin Hood – and he liked them. But whenever he picked up a book for himself the words wriggled like worms on the page. He could never piece the patterns together. Besides, all those tales of dead worlds, all those thoughts about thinking, all that sitting down, reading. No good can come of it. They're stuck outside the walls of the city, fighting dogs and bandits. That's the only story they should worry about.

The warriors of Wick Wood say they're at war. They say it's time to stop trading with the enemy and start trading with each other. Not old books and paper, things of real worth. Objects of *action*. They say Pegger's the right man to take the war up the Lea for them. That's right. They said *man*. Pegger feels inside his cloak for his purchase. He takes out the gun and turns it in his hands. He's never shot one before. Hell, he's never seen one outside of a comic book before today. He pushes the muzzle through the reeds and aims it at the punter grasping his way onto the river bank.

'Bang,' he says.

*

Under the arch, Heraldine kneels before Naja and Badru. In payment for her pleasures she offers up a handful of coins from her smock pocket. 'This is all I've got. It's not easy to get these. In the city we don't have money. It's all electronic. These coins, they're worthless you know.'

'We choose what we make precious,' says Naja. 'You can fix value to an old shoe, long as others see it the same. But be prepared to let go the precious thing you love. Tide comes, tide goes. It's your soul you must protect, not shiny rock, not the systems of men, not them electric screens that pleasure you.'

Heraldine reaches for a small wooden board, striated with slender metal strips. It's Naja's karimba. Naja stops her hand before she can touch the instrument. 'You cannot take, but you can borrow widja ears.'

Naja picks up the karimba and her long, double-jointed thumbs flex and bow over the keys. A sweet, shimmering melody fills the archway. Fighting back tears, Heraldine curls into a foetal ball and hugs her pain tight. She misses the sound of things rubbing together and the miraculous vibrations which are born in those moments. It takes her back to a time long ago when there was a piano in her grandmother's apartment, scarred with scratches and dents, reeking of furniture polish. Even back then, it was rare for anyone in the city to own a physical musical instrument. She remembers the way she pressed the keys and soft hammers thumped on wire. Those imperfections, bum notes and tiny flaws in the tuning which made the music so human. That magic is recreated in every stroke of Naja's thumbs.

Coiled in her reverie, Heraldine doesn't notice Pegger push the second punter through the slit in the briars and follow through after him, nerves buzzing with Büyü powder. The gun feels cold and urgent against the small of his back. The sight of the fat woman grovelling at the merch heap only stiffens his resolve. He must carry out what he promised the Wick Woodlanders he would do. There's no going back now.

Pegger nudges the new punter further inside the archway. He is as tubby as the woman, but his face is gaunt and jaundiced, with dark circles round his eyes. He rubs his arm as if to brush away the filth of Pegger's touch, and scans the graffiti with a snarl of disgust.

Naja senses trouble. She stops her playing and says to the man, 'Welcome.'

Ignoring her, the man strides over to the woman curled on the floor by the book pile. He stares down at her, trembling. 'Heraldine! How could you?'

'Bry!' Heraldine uncoils like a startled snake and beholds her husband with terror.

Bry stoops down to her, but falls short of touching her face. 'What have they done to you?' He turns to Naja and Badru, 'What have you done to her? If you have . . . '

'I wanted to see for myself,' says Heraldine.

Bry's sallow cheeks blossom with rage as he stomps around her in a circle, waving his arms. 'What kind of man could be driven so low as to follow his own wife? . . . And then find her grubbing around in a pit of squalor like a rat? I thought you were having an affair. But this? This is disgusting. If this gets out . . . '

'Please, Bry!'

'You mean to ruin me!'

'It's you ruining *me*, Bry,' wails Heraldine. 'You haven't been in the same room as me for months. I can't love a screen, Bry. I can't.'

'That's why you came here? To make a point? You stupid woman.'

'Look, this innt our business,' says Badru, feeling Naja bristle. 'You better go.'

'Don't tell me what to do, rat boy!' yells Bry, 'It'll be your fucking business when they hear about this! They'll tear down the flood barriers and drown this place to hell.' He hauls Heraldine to her feet and begins to drag her, flailing and weeping, across the concrete towards the exit.

Pegger cackles as he dances gleefully from foot to foot, sweet adrenaline fizzing through him. This is all unfolding better than he could ever have hoped. It's like this was meant to happen.

'What are you laughing at, boy?' says Bry, struggling to keep his wife on her feet. 'I don't think you quite understand who I am.'

'I know who you are,' Pegger draws his gun, 'you're the dead man.' Bry cowers behind his wife, tightening his arm across her bosom, pinning her to him.

'Don't, Pegger, dontcha do that,' says Naja..

'Better listen to her.' Bry holds up a small black box, flickering with luminescent data. 'You're being watched. All they need is one excuse, one good reason to destroy you.'

A moving picture appears on the screen of the box. Pegger sees an image of himself staring back, the gun gleaming in the gloom. So this was one of those famous all-seeing 'screens' the punters liked to gibber and moan about. He can't fathom their problem. The screen makes him look wild and beautiful, like one of those warriors from the streets of old London he's seen in picture books. Grinning for the camera, he pulls the trigger.

A bright flash scorches the archway. Heraldine slides from Bry's grip and sits on the floor with a thump. She glances sorrowfully at Naja, opening her mouth to say something. Blood begins to gush from her lips, spilling down her floral smock. She puts her hands to her chest, feeling for the hole, a quizzical expression on her face. Slowly, she falls onto her side, blood pooling towards the merch.

Pegger watches, enthralled. He didn't mean to shoot the woman, but it's all going to mean the same in the end. He steps closer to Bry, gun raised.

'Pegger! Put it down!' Naja's voice is tiny, childlike, in a way Pegger has never heard before. She sounds like a little girl in a fairytale storybook, and he's the big bad King. He shrugs and fires again. The bullet splinters the brick above Bry's shoulder. Bry scrambles desperately through the briars. Pegger tries to follow, but Badru blocks his way, spear pointed at his chest. They can hear the crunch of Bry's running feet on dead wood and the panic of crows as dogs barrel across the marsh, excited by the gunshots.

'It's done now innt,' says Pegger, pointing the gun at Badru's head. 'Lemme go after him.'

'You done enough,' says Badru. 'The dogs''ll take him. Stay with us and we'll work it out.'

'There innt no more us, only war,' says Pegger. 'Lemme go.'

'Shoot if you like, I am not afraid to die.'

Pegger swings the gun in Naja's direction. 'Then I shoot her instead innt.'

Naja's eyes are molten as she gets to her feet and stretches tall beneath the graffiti ceiling, feeling sudden kinship with the ancestors depicted on the arc of brick, like she's strapped to the wheel of time with them, turning, turning, faster and faster until they're a solid halo of colour.

Shaking his head sadly. Badru lowers the spear. Pegger shoves him aside and races from the arch with a whoop, waving the gun above his head. Outside the bullmastiffs break out in a frenzy of snarling and gnashing. Quickly, Badru and Naja throw the sack over the glowstick and clutch each other in the safety of darkness. They hear screams, then Pegger's gun cracking the night.

After a short while, the gun falls silent.

*

In the days that follow, Naja and Badru collect the merch from their stashes across Walthamstow Marsh, whistling out to each other for signs of dogs and bandits. From sinkholes in the bog they haul plastic bags of poetry, novels, magazines, newspapers, flyers and junk mail. They gather up the penny whistles, maracas and casabas stuffed in cavities across the old aqueduct and buried beneath the feet of pylons. In the relative safety of the MegaRink, they arrange the merch in piles on a series of rafts they've bound together, then wrap it in tarpaulin and secure it tight.

When it's peaceful enough, Naja plays her karimba and sings her dubs while Badru keeps watch over the valley from the uppermost girders. Most nights the Lea is a tumult of shouts and calls, barking dogs and the occasional burst of gunfire. Airships rise over the silvery walls of Tech City and drift across the marsh. Naja and Badru huddle for cover when the searchlights explode off the exposed beams and splintered roof panels of the MegaRink. The airships move north to Tottenham, then turn and head south towards the shattered concrete wasteland of Hackney Marsh, then the broken towers of Stratford, beams of light tracing wild figures running through the scrub.

One evening there are hollers from below. A group of Wick Woodland warriors are gathered near their raft, holding something aloft on a stick.

'Naja!' they call, mockingly. 'Naja! We know you up there, Naja! Your boy Pegger is a hero! Come say hello.'

Naja doesn't need to climb down to know what is on the end of the stick. Badru's stricken face is enough. From high above the marsh he watches his old friend's severed head, mouth open, wide eyed, bobbing in the torchlight above the heads of the warriors as they march south.

The next day, figures in white protective suits and visors swarm across the river from Robin Hood point. They collect up the rafts and burn them on a pyre. They remove Heraldine's body from the bridge and what's left of Bry on the riverbank, then float them across the river, attended by mourners in black wet suits. Naja and Badru hear an explosion. Holding hands they watch the remains of the railway bridge plunge into the silt, smoke coiling from the crumbled archway, crows shrieking through an ashen sky towards the sun.

Later a squadron of airships amasses above the city and moves out towards the Thames Estuary. Naja knows well enough from her reading what this means. She knows about the rising sea levels and the great barrier which protected Old London and still holds back the waters. She knows from her dreams what will come next. The distant explosions will herald the beginning of a great flood.

But she has her raft. She has the last books in London. She has her trusted friend, Badru.

She is ready.

After decades of stagnation the Lea is on the move once again, swollen with water pouring in from the sea. The currents dislodge a deep graveyard of car parts, dead dogs, rats, cows, horses and humans, plastic bags, driftwood, nappies, bottles and cans. A black soup of silt, trash and bones seeps across Walthamstow Marsh. Watery tendrils snake through rivets, trenches and abandoned stash holes. Within days, a network of water channels forms a shimmering lattice across the landscape. The channels widen and interlink, the water running faster, forcing down rotten trees, undermining the earth beneath unstable ruins and pylons, toppling them into the swell. Water laps the rubble of the demolished riverside apartments and gushes through the ground level of the MegaRink whereNaja's raft afloats, tethered with rope. For a final time she and Badru look out from the roof across the Lea. They see a lake where Hackney Marsh used to be. Even the treetops of the Wick Woodland have vanished beneath the water's surface. The last remnants of the marsh – pylon tips and the tallest trees – are dark blots on the border between water and sky, like dead flies slammed under a book.

'Is this what you foresaw?' asks Badru.

'All is becoming one,' says Naja,'and when it does so, there will be no more edge, no inside, no outside, only heaven.'

'Or hell.'

'Yes,' says Naja. 'Or hell.'

They descend slowly to their raft and clamber on board. Badru hunches among the book piles, spear raised, watching for signs of the enemy, though they've heard no human noise in days and no more airships fly from the city. Naja casts off and the raft drifts across a wide, fast-moving Lea, invigorated by long lost tides, pulsing with new currents. Gulls wheel in the sky. Salt wafts through the air. Deep below them, strange water creatures wriggle and squirm over the drowned marshes. The distant horizon is a bleeding heart crushed by heavy clouds.

Slowly, hopefully, they row towards it.

XXII

Epilogue

Two weeks after I handed the first draft of my collected marsh stories into my publishers, Hendrix and I joined a crowd gathered outside The Princess of Wales pub by the Lea Bridge for the Beating of the Bounds. It was the 5th of May 2013, a hundred and fifty years (and eight months) after the unfortunate Whipple and Hazlehurst fell into the Navigation at the very same spot. I was handed my ceremonial stripped willow bark as local historian Katy Andrews explained how this ancient ritual re-established common rights over the land by marking the boundaries of the Lammas Lands and the three parishes of Hackney, Leyton and Walthamstow. It was a bright afternoon, sunlight glinting off the floating bottles in the water, sweating islets of mulch, sparkling blossom on the trees. The Princess of Wales beer garden was full of people staring at us in bewilderment. A helicopter circled overhead, infusing the atmosphere with a pre-revolutionary tension as a man banged a drum and we began to follow Katy towards the marshes.

Numbering over sixty people, this was one of the biggest gatherings the organisers had seen for such an event in twenty years, reflecting a ground swell of interest in the marshes, with so many new threats and challenges looming. It included members of the Save Lea Marshes Group, the Millfields Blog, the Lammas Defence Committee, familiar faces from the Leyton Marsh basketball protests the previous summer, children, interested locals, interested non-locals and disinterested dogs. The faces were all friendly, except for that of a tall, grey-coiffered man leaning stiffly against the wall of the pub, watching me with furrowed brow, scribbling in a notepad. He looked a lot how I'd imagine Octavious Whipple would appear in middle age. When I stared back at him he made no attempt to shift his gaze. Did I know him? My skin crawled. I tugged Hendrix's lead and we pushed further ahead into the group, which was now on the move.

We shuffled through the gates of the Middlesex Filter beds in a scene reminiscent of Ada's illustrations for my story *The Raving Dead*. It was strange to be part of a crowd. I'd spent the previous five years in isolation, walking the marshes alone every day, then writing about them in my study. I'd laboured under the illusion that I was a solitary observer, separate from the rest of humanity, scribing a narrative of the marshes from my egotistical tower. Perhaps that's how I started out. But now that I walked in step with equally enthused marsh lovers, clutching my willow branch, I realised I had undergone a metamorphosis. I was no longer a passive chronicler but an active node of marsh consciousness, carrying out its will. I had been assimilated. The landscape was dictating my behaviour, not the other way round. It no longer felt like I had chosen to write this book. The marshes had impelled it to exist. They had been playing me, right from the start.

I understood this to be true as soon as Katy Andrews began dangling the children.

The traditional method of marking the boundaries is to tip a child upside down and lower its head onto the marker. The Old River Lea is such a boundary, being a border between warring Saxon and Danish nations, between the countries of Middlesex and Essex, between the old parishes of Hackney and Leyton, between the modern Greater London boroughs. At the Friends Bridge a seven year old boy was held by his waist and his head dipped towards the ground. I experienced a flashback to 2008 when Mr Mastiff held me upside down over the Lea the day that Hendrix fell into the icy water. In Chapter One I described it as a baptism. Only now did I realise how true that was. I was a child who knew nothing of the significance of the landscape I was about to explore, wholly unaware that Mr Mastiff and I were echoing an ancient local ritual. At that moment of initiation I could never have conceived that I would write stories, blogs and poetry about the marsh. But it all began right there. The act of being dangled over a river by a stranger was the first of the many tales the marshes have commuted to me. Without them, I would remain a blank page. Thinking about it, I would have never found the marshes in the first place if I'd not bought a cocker spaniel puppy. Did that make Hendrix my muse? My spirit guide? Watching him munch on a dried turd, I wondered. *Perhaps you get the spirit guide you deserve.*

'For good or bad, he's yours,' said a voice. That strange coiffuered man stood by my shoulder, looking at my dog with a crooked smile. 'That's the wonderful thing about Hendrix.'

'Sorry, have we met?' I said.

'Oh, I know plenty about your adventures,' he said. 'I've been tracking you both very closely.'

Panic flushed my head. I imagined him secretly stalking me through the undergrowth with his notebook. 'I'm not sure I . . . what do you mean, 'tracking'?'

'Don't you have a blog? A Twitter account?'' He placed a hand on my shoulder. 'What is there *not* to know? You and I share a mutual interest.'

Oh, this was just great. Someone else writing about the marshes at exactly the same time as me. Subscribing to my blog. Following my tweets. Stealing my ideas, most likely. 'You're a writer?'

'Ha ha, more of a ghost writer,' he said. 'Don't worry. I am where you are not.'

I tried to smile through my nausea. This was the last person I wanted to meet today. For all I knew he had the same bloody publisher. After an interminable moment staring at each other in silence, I pretended that someone had waved me over, made my apologies and scuttled away.

As the tour continued and Katy regaled the group with historical details, I grew even more uncomfortable. She told many of the stories I had discovered during my time writing about the marshes. She also revealed facts that were new to me. For instance, that the wedge of land at the top corner of Hackney Marsh north of the Friends Bridge, where Albie Moxley, dressed as a bear, fled from an approaching tiger on the 26th December 1981, is not part of the marshes at all but an anomalous patch owned by the National Grid. She also described how in the 1950s elephants could be seen on Walthamstow Marsh when they were taken for exercise by staff from the circus which came to the Lea Bridge Road.

Elephants? How could I know about bears and crocodiles, but not about the elephants? Not even my hallucinating restaurateur, Iriz, in *The Fires of London* saw elephants. I looked across at the ghost writer, listening to Katy with his eyes closed, no doubt gathering all of the facts for some damned rival book. Sweat broke out on my brow. How many others like me and were writing about the marshes? How many more stories were there in this place? How deep down did it go? Had I even scratched the surface?

I felt queasy with vertigo, as if standing at the lip of an interminable well. All these marshland tales I had discovered and invented – the secret histories, local myths, and flights of imagination – they seemed like tiny drops of rain falling onto the surface of this prehistoric river which swelled with ancient memories, each water molecule a life lived. And this was just one patch of land in London. The whole city, the whole country, the whole world is full of stories. Every single human being is a node channelling the landscape in which they live, their unique snowflake narratives piling into great white drifts, rising higher than mountains, stretching toward the horizon of an ever-expanding universe.

That day on the Friends Bridge I looked deep into the Old River Lea, swirling through a gulley of pylons, sludge pipes, hogweed and poplars, en-route to the Thames and, ultimately, the ocean.

As I gazed, I had a dream.

XXIII

A Dream Life of Hackney Marshes: A Libretto

A Hole In London

There is a hole in London. An ancient marshland strewn with ruins, rubble and wild flowers. It swallows up the city's time.

Victorian machines decay in overgrown filter beds. Lost footballs from long abandoned games stick against the canalside. Herons scan the water in a flooded bomb crater. Wind blows the ketamine debris of an outdoor rave. Umbrellas of giant hogweed block out the sun.

London's past, present and future is scattered around. But you have to stop and listen. You must put your ear to the fragments if you wish to eavesdrop on the city's dream.

Flight

I wake beneath a railway bridge in the morning mist to the sound of beating air. A fat swan skitters on the canal, crying to fly . . .

The moon hangs on the threshold of dawn. A narrowboat piled with coal bags and potted tulips glides by. All is well and nothing is as it seems.

I walk in the morning mist to the sound of beating air. A fat swan lifts from the water, crying to fly . . .

Beneath this railway arch a man once built a wooden aeroplane and wheeled it onto Walthamstow Marsh. Drunk with hope, the crowd watched it lurch in the sky.

That instant, the heavens opened and filled the marsh with new dreams.

Water Works

Thick with slicks of bottles and cans, the sick green canal slides over the Weir, becomes a river again.

She spins down a deep gulley, wide and black with mud. She swells around rocky islets. She gathers her lost traces.

Trees bow at her passing, as she reclaims her dominion.

Angel

And then I see her, rising from the scrub, crackling with power. My head tells me it's just another electricity pylon but – she's different. I can't take my eyes off her.

SONG:

Her name was Angel
You can laugh, you can mock
To me she was unconstructed
She had come from above
Go and tell the Captain, when he calls her by her name
And the man upon the mountain
That their fear and love is just a game
I grew bored of watching wrecking balls, dismantling
And the upturned shopping trolleys, discarded
Now hear triangles echoing,
Echoing . . .

Black cable whips from her arms to embrace me. I gasp at the poetry in her spirals of steel. She fires sunbeams through her gaping geometry. I touch her legs, thrilling at the thought of the volts running through her.

SONG:

Her name was Angel
I was cold, I was lost
I lay beneath her, trembling
From the power of her touch
There he stood beneath her and he knew her by her name
And the man beside the mountain
And his fear and love was just the same
I grew bored of watching wrecking balls, dismantling
And the upturned shopping trolleys, discarded
Now hear triangles, echoing,
Echoing

Her name was Angel
You can laugh, you can mock
To me she was unconstructed
She had come from above
Go and tell the Captain, when he calls her by her name
And the man upon the mountain
That their fear and love is just a game

There was a time before I fell in love with a pylon on Hackney Marsh. But that time is gone.

Echo Bombs

I walk away from the ruins of my heart across empty football pitches. Beneath the soil, rubble from the Blitz. Rain bleeds through layers of brick and bone. A chamber echoes with the voices of the dead.

I hear bombs.

Pylon March

Look out from the marsh! Behold strange towers on the horizon!

The Olympian citadel rises in a helicopter swarm. A hunchbacked helter-skelter prowls Stratford. The Illuminati eye of Canary Wharf winks from the Isle of Dogs. Hackney's tower-blocks glow pink in the setting sun. The Shard, Gherkin and Heron Towers are sentinels at the City's gates.

All along the Lea, mad London roars in a frenzy of demolition and construction. Hammers strike the sky. Sparks fly.

A parade of pylons blasts electricity into the city. Slaves manacled to each other with loops of glass and cable, outcast and forsaken. I join their march across the marshes.

Song of Pigeons

Beneath the railway bridge by the old copper mill at dusk, I sit by the still water and listen to the song of pigeons.

Beneath the railway bridge by the old copper mill at midnight, I sleep by the dark water and dream of Hackney Marshes.

XXIV

Appendix: Soundchronicity Walks

Anybody who has listened to music while walking knows the joy of starring in their own soundtrack. Some days I feel the urge to disconnect from the marshland and indulge in some fantasy. With my iPod on I walk at a furious pace to techno, dub and psych rock. The landscape becomes a painted backdrop to my personal concert. Purists say that this behaviour dislocates you from other people; it creates a barrier between you and the world; it's self-indulgent. But sometimes that's exactly what's required. Used in moderation, I'm all for it. Millions of people walk the world with headphones on. Who are we to deny the validity of this experience? Music creates a psychic space into which people can step when the rhythms of daily life get too much.

I believe it's also possible to use music as a tool of engagement with your landscape, if you turn the volume down so that the sounds of the environment are audible and choose evocative music that has space between the beats and melodies. Ambient, drone, music concrete, minimal techno, experimental electronics, library music, sound collage all work for me. When I take this music onto the marshes I don't obliterate the rhythms of London, I alter them. The music blends with the sound of wind, hooting horns, dog barks and disembodied human voices, creating a unique audio mix, never to be repeated. At times it's hard to distinguish those sounds that are in the music from those transmitted by the city. The distinction becomes meaningless. The music mutates the landscape and the landscape mutates the music. They become one and the same.

I call these experiences *soundchronicities*. They create a space where mind, music and environment intersect. It's a magical world, liberated from everyday reality, and utterly transient. It exists for a moment in time, somewhere between you and the artist, mediated by the landscape. You can never revisit this place. Nobody can ever share the experience, even with the same music walking the same route. But what you can do is write down your observations.

This is what I have done over the past couple of years. My methodology is simple: walk the marsh with no pre-ordained plan, listen to the music at a volume that doesn't obliterate external sounds, and note down any interesting impressions. Try it yourself. You will have your own taste music, but should you wish for inspiration I've included a list of my favourite music for walking at the end of this book (see Notes).

1. Magick on the River Lea

Jon Brooks – *Music For Thomas Carnacki (Radiophonic Themes and Abstracts)* [Café Kaput]

Thomas Carnacki is a supernatural detective from a series of short stories by William Hope Hodgson. Jon Brook's album of haunting radiophonic

instrumentals is a soundtrack to a reading of Hodgson's story 'The Gateway Of The Monster'.

A gothic harpsichord strikes up as I head down the Lee towpath with Hendrix. He is unusually slow today, grazing for breadscraps and dog-shit in the verges. Some days it's like taking a sheep for a walk. A shroud of grey silk hangs over the marsh. The Lee is eerily still. 'Valse Vargo', a haunting waltz, decays in a wash of echo. Two geese, facing opposite directions, guard the barrier to the Lea Bridge. In 'Cheyene Walk' ascending bleeps rise from bed of electronic chirrups. Beyond the filter beds, a moorhen stands on the canal's surface. This ornithological Christ has impossibly bright blue feet. I'm listening to 'A Curious Undulation'. A ripple disturbs the glassy canal. It suggests the aftermath of a drowning. A dead fish floats by, embedded in a scab of putrefied weed.

I walk across the marsh to queasy strings submerged in tape hiss, electronic motifs heavy with echo and tumbling piano. The atmosphere takes a turn for the darker at 'Electric Pentangle'. I pass an old man walking a terrier. It emits an unearthly snarl. For a moment I think it's the dog going for Hendrix. When I yank off my earphones I realise it's the strangled electronics, not the dog. This blending of internal and external sound increases the deeper I go into the woodland. 'Certain Manifestations' is the sound of Satan gargling in a howling wind. The crows join the cacophony of moog shrieks.

The most eerie thing about *Music for Thomas Carnacki* is a tinkling piano loop, sampled off the second edition of the Buddha Machine, a plastic box like an old FM radio which plays ambient loops. This was the only piece of music that would get Venus, my second daughter, to sleep in her first six months of life. She cried all day and all night with colic. By the time we discovered she had lactose intolerance it was too late. She'd learned to scream herself to sleep. Only that particular loop on the *Buddha Machine II* calmed her. We'd place it by her cot, sit in the living room and hear it coming through the baby monitor, mingled with her cries. That melody is a soundtrack to sleep deprivation. Hearing it in Brooks' piece by the burbling river, the memories flood back. It's uncomfortable, the distance between myself and that self. Life seemed so unbearable at the time. I have forgotten how much of it I have forgotten. This memory gap now bridged by Brooks' soundtrack to a supernatural detective story. 'The Gateway of the Monster'. Welcome to fatherhood.

2. Widdershins in Walthamstow

The Psychogeographic Commission – *Widdershins*

A 26 minute recording of the Glasgow subway train as it moves anti-clockwise (widdershins) beneath the city. The field recording is underscored by electronic drones. The Commission say: 'Beginning and ending at Hillhead Station, we recorded over the period of totality on the winter solstice eclipse 2010, the first time a total eclipse has fallen on a winter solstice since the days of Prophet Peden (1638).'

This is a mistake. It won't work. On weekdays the marsh is relatively empty. I might meet a few dog walkers, a couple of Hasidic Jews bowed in conversation, boatpeople chopping wood on the towpath. But I have picked a bad time to experiment with drone music. It's a sunny summer Sunday evening. The place is bustling. Tennis players shout in Springfield Park. Couples skip gaily by the river. Eau de Cologne wafts from white-shirted blokes heading to the pub. On Walthamstow Marsh groups of twentysomethings huddle, simian tribes in the long grass.

The place has never looked less like itself. That mix of the mystical and mundane has been replaced by scenes from an iPhone advert. In this context it's odd listening to the opening of *Widdershins*, recorded deep underground during a Winter Solstice. The Glasgow subway train judders. Wheels squeak at the first stop. Doors open. A drone swells in the gap. The frenetic rave bleep of sliding doors. Then *woosh*, the train is off. I take a route through the wild woodland away from the picnic tables and come out at the north corner of Walthamstow Marsh, an empty green triangle alongside the railway lines.

That's when it clicks. The national express train from Clapton cuts across the marsh, windows glinting. At the same point in my headphones the Glasgow subway train pulls away from its stop. I watch a London train in brilliant sunlight, its clattering wheels blending with the Glasgow underground train. I realise suddenly that I am walking clockwise round the marsh, listening to an anti-clockwise journey in Scotland, recorded in another time, another season. My eyes are overground in summer, my ears underground in winter. My body is in London, my mind in Glasgow. I twist the layers of time-space like a Rubik's Cube.

Another train comes in the opposite direction – widdershins! – moving towards the Victorian bridge to Clapton. The exhausted Glasgow train hauls itself off to the next stop with a huff and hiss. The two are now in full flow with synchronised clattering. At that moment a dimensional rift opens up. I plunge my arm through the rift until my fist emerges in Scotland, rats pouring out of the vent and scattering down Buchanan Street to screams. An old Glaswegian woman hobbles past with her dog and – cackling sadistically – I flip her into the bowels of London as a blood sacrifice. I push myself through the tear in time-space until

I wear England as a thick woollen dress and Scotland as a summer hat. My feet stick into the Channel. I begin to stride with purpose across Europe.

Separated from its ceremonial context and laid over an alternative topography, *Widdershins* unleashes a moment of glorious synchronicity. Sound allows you be in two locations at once. It's a method of teleportation, much in the same way as smell enables time travel, that feeling of being there when your nose gets a whiff of the past. The Pyschogeographical Commission's fusing of real and imagined landscape allows you to transcend dimensions.

3. The Topography of London's Sky

Keith Fullerton Whitman – *Generator* [Root Strata]

Whitman sets in motion a series of self modulating electronic sequences. Pulses, bleeps and drones organise themselves into cosmic odysseys.

On today's walk I am uncomfortably aware of how the mechanics of the body influence perception. Our eyes have evolved to scan the horizon for prey and opportunity. The horizontal plane is our hunting ground. Our heads swing more easily from side to side than up and down. A baby learns to shake her head for 'no' before she learns to nod 'yes'.

It's difficult to walk while staring up. You become disconnected from your natural compass. It's hard to gauge distance and direction. Your choice of landmarks is reduced to lampposts, Church spires and tower blocks. An aeroplane at 30,000 feet becomes clearer than the DO NO ENTER sign, dog-shit and manhole ahead of you.

So I spend my days looking *around* at things: cars, trees, strangers, walls, the contents of my fridge, the expression of concern on my family's faces. I rarely pay attention to what's above me. I miss the *upness* of things.

Walking by the Old River Lea, listening to Keith Fullerton Whitman's *Generator* on my iPod, I get an overwhelming urge to look up. As the binary bleeps unfold and expand I lift up my eyes to beginning of the rest of the universe.

'That's it!' I remark to Hendrix, who I can hear snuffling somewhere close. 'For the rest of today I'm only looking at the sky!'

I stride onto Hackney Marsh with my head tilted like a solar panel, oscillations in my ears, calling 'Hendrix, Hendrix, Hendrix!' to keep him close. In the trees I can navigate easily, but on the playing fields I lose the natural scaffolding. It as if I'm floating above ground. There's only me and *what's up*.

Whitman gives these spiralling electronic sequences their own life, creating a seemingly accidental sonic universe. Of course, this music is guided by the hand of Whitman, the pantheistic god who gets the ball rolling. He sets the parameters, cuts, arranges, selects.

Like Fullerton Whitman's music, the London sky seems organic but is shaped by human intervention. It's only *like* nature. Stare up and try to imagine you're anywhere in the world. You can't. This vista is London born and bred. There's always a crane, pylon or tower stabbing at the periphery of your vision. A blimp floats above Leyton. Aeroplanes trace the geometry of routes dictated by stressed air-traffic controllers. Circling the earth, a halo of space rubbish, satellites and dead Russian astronaut dogs. **Trashcan Infinity.**

The London sky is an edgeland between earth and infinity. A gateway terrain of cloud mountains, blue lakes and islands, striated with contrails and stained by pollution. As 'Generator''s self-perpetuating synths pulse and fornicate the universe expands. Cosmic battles rage as the planet hurtles through dark matter and solar winds. I watch the sun burn a hole through black cloud skulking among the cirrus. Suddenly I don't feel like walking any more. This A-to-B lark seems pointless, considering the vastness of everything. I sit on the green grass. I lie on my back. My body gives way to computer dreams.

4. Analogue Man

Ekoplekz - *Memowrekz* [Mordant Music]

33 tracks of twisted analogue synthesiser, spanning almost two hours.

I cut through Millfields Park as 'Visions of Purdown' rumbles from a field of static. The afternoon is pregnant with cloud. A dog walker approaches. I know her. I could explain, 'Sorry, can't stop, I'm conducting sonic experiments.' But I'd come across as a bit of a prick. So I change tack and scutter across the park to the 'Plekziglass''s urgent seagull cries. My head fills with wah-wah. I pass beneath the Lea Bridge as 'Moonbase Siege' kicks off like a John Carpenter soundtrack. It's an appropriate entry into Marshworld. On the Lea canal towpath the rustic daily life clashes with the heavy industry overhead. Beyond the narrowboats, airliners emerge from a smog shroud over the Olympic City. I listen to 'D-3 Chamber''s razorblade synth as I walk beneath power cables. A sign tells fishermen to beware of electrocution.

A seam of dub and funk runs through *Memowrekz* but it's submerged, as if coming from a chamber beneath the filter beds. The ghost of a Victorian worker beneath the central culvert pulls levers and – for the first time in 100 years – the sluice gates open, spilling viscous ooze into the canal. I pass a rusted cargo barge half-sunk in the duckweed. Fuck the walk. This music is so heavy I want to drag myself onto its foredeck and bathe in ozone. Ageing runners appear on the towpath. They move awkwardly to *Memowrekz*'s synth judder, parodies of Steve Austin's slow-motion running in *The Six Million Dollar Man*. A man with crutches looks on from a bench.

Three thoughts strike me in quick succession:

1. Man is a flawed machine.
2. Analogue is the music of flawed machines.
3. We make a good team on the pre-digital marsh.

I'm carried across the playing fields by 'Fixation', bleeping over an insistent bass line. I enter the woodland by the Old River Lea. This is the Proterozone, a remnant of a time before canalisation, before industry, before me and Ekoplekz. I'm dive-bombed by two butterflies. Something slithers in the undergrowth beside me. A sonic lizard seeking a mate. 'Mindreaver' wigs out with what sounds like Iggy Pop's 'Nightclubbin' guitar solo submerged in the noise. I'm not sure whether I'm experiencing Ekoplekz's musical memories now or my own. I hurry over Friends Bridge to the underpass beneath the Lea Bridge Road. 'The Sinister Sponge' plays me past a graffiti-daubed concrete obelisk. I stop to gaze at the corpse of a spider in its own web, surrounded by uneaten flies. A visionary ensnared by her failed Grand Scheme.

'Toxic Shock' is in my ears by the blackberry bushes on the aqueduct path. Its sinister death-ray shrivels the fruit on the branches. A stopped train full of blank faces stare at me from above on the railway bridge. Skeletal turrets loom from the reservoir. I press on, listening to 'Elektrotrakz', its distorted voices struggling through the noise. I hit the path toward the Springfield marina, woozy in the ketamine shimmer of 'Electronic Medication'. The sun languishes in a bed of cloud. Magpies dance in the air. A flock of geese flies in a 'V' formation. Two stragglers try to catch up and complete the shape. Their system is imperfect, but it works.

A thought strikes me. Nature is a series of fantastic mistakes. The analogue electronics in *Memowrekz* are the sounds of the living machine: beautiful, flawed, mysterious.

5. Transhuman Hackney

TVO – *Red Night* [Broken20]

An album of drones, tone pieces and broken techno featuring a sample of William Burroughs reading from Cities of the Red Night, *the book which inspired the music.*

Red Night begins with a barely audible hiss, no louder than London's perma-drone: traffic, distant drilling, the pulse of planes. The stripped banks of the Old Lea River are haunted by railway power lines and warehouses.

The river runs with the hum of 'Tamaghis'. A concrete ledge is draped with root tendrils. A black poplar splayed like a charred star fish. A photographer with a tripod stalks through the dead leaves. This track creeps up on you, ever more intense, until Hackney drowns in white noise. The banks brim with rubbish. The natural order is defeated. The Lea is alive instead with transhuman sound, a bastard fusion of man and machine. Forklifts crunch through pallets. Container trucks rumble. In the future these things carry on without us. Machines feed on our leftover energy. Electricity dribbles from snapped power-lines. An eternal loop of pop music crackles from a radio. The DJ is a corpse with his cranium slumped on the play button.

'Ba'dan' is awash with aquatic bubbling and static crunch. A digger claws through broken boxes. The reverse lights of a truck in New Spitalfields Market flash to the beat. Everything is sucked downriver in a weary funk. The East Marsh, post-Olympics, is a burial mound of soil. No birds sing. The artificial bird song at the end of 'Ba'dan' replaces what is missing in reality. I hear a squeaky wheel. I take off the headphones. It's not from the track – it's some kind of bird or a broken trolley in New Spitalfields. I don't know. I have lost the distinction between the natural and the synthetic.

Nobody is walking on Hackney Marsh. Only a line painter van doing angular circuits in an icy wind. The relentless clicks of 'Yass Wadda' freeze me out of my own thoughts.

Two helicopters chase each other across the sky to the robotic techno of 'Waghdas'. The track is powered by a whirring fan generator. Loud bass pulses. I turn up the volume as I stride across the football pitches. A man comes towards me, pushing a white line painting machine. He is one of Hackney's Nazca men, delineating the post-human desert. A priest representing the old religion of manual labour.

I walk along the eastern flank of Hackney Marsh and stand before Landmark Heights, the Headquarters of the Kingdom of God. The tower block looms over stripped trees. Disembodied voices echo rhythmically over fragmented drums. After the desolation of The Lea, apocalyptic tribes are flourishing in the wastelands of Hackney.

'Ghadis' begins with motorbike revs, or the sawing of trees. The red wall of the ruined coal power station broods over a recycling plant. The machines are alive. Everything masticated, consumed, made anew. I am marching to the beat.

I listen to 'B-23' by the Navigation approaching the Lea Bridge Road. A white teenager in a Kaftan frantically scoops rubbish from the verge, hurls it onto the path. When he opens his mouth as I pass, he speaks with the voice of William Burroughs, telling the tale from the novel *Cities of the Red Night* of the sick, blotched boy presented to the doctor. Sexual delirium, says the doctor, send him to isolation. Humankind is the epidemic. When we are gone, only the line painters will remain. Self-driving forklifts will crash through pallets, trash the remaining stock.

Everything must go.

Notes

Entropy Junction

The landscape described in this chapter has mostly disappeared. The crumbling towpath at the bottom of Millfields Park was restored in advance of the Olympics. The warehouses between Millfields and Springfield Park have almost all been demolished. The concrete peninsula known as Essex Wharf now boasts a residential apartment block.

1.   The green man painted beneath the railway bridge near Springfield Park is a symbol found in many ancient churches and cathedrals. Nobody is sure of his exact meaning and origin. Many pagans link him to the cycle of birth, life, death and decay. He has also been linked to Robin Hood (perhaps a reference to the Robin Hood Point crossing nearby, where the Robin Hoood pub once stood) and many other figures, including The Green Knight, Wodwose and many Celtic gods. He often appears in May Day celebrations as a symbol of Merrie Olde England.

2.   The dragon is another symbol of earth and nature. Dragons are also protectors of the City of London. Guardians of borders.

3.   Many centuries before this shootout I witnessed, Millfields Park was the scene of an ancient skirmish. The Battle of Hackney was alleged to have taken place there in 527AD. Octa, King of

Kent was having trouble with Erchewin, founder of Essex, who had turned against him. Octa gathered his forces in Hackney for a march on London but was surprised when Erchewin's supporters came out to meet them there for a pitch battle.

The Memory of Water

Elements of this chapter have been excerpted from 'Monsters of Hackney & Walthamstow Marsh', an essay by the author which appears in *The Ashgate Research Companion to Paranormal Cultures*, edited by Jenzen, O and Munt, S.R (Farnham: Ashgate 2013) pp. 398-399. © 2013

The 2005 BBC reports on the Lea Crocodile can be found at: http://news.bbc.co.uk/1/hi/england/london/4748335.stm and also http://news.bbc.co.uk/1/hi/england/london/4748335.stm

Information on the Viking raid up the Lea can be found on the excellent Lea Bridge Heritage website on this page: http://www.leabridge.org.uk/myths/king-alfred-and-the-viking.html

Life Between Epochs

This story has its origin in a Twitter conversation I had with author David Southwell and Pynchon In Public. We began by discussing micronations and, somehow, it led to the invention of an independent state based entirely on a narrowboat. David came up with the name the Unmoored Manor of Mutating Manifestation and I thank him for letting me use it in my story.

A Walk By The River

At the time of publication the safe is still there, though it has since been prized open.

The Most Peculiar Vanishing of Messrs Whipple and Hazlehurst

Reader, please take note. I'm not responsible for any historical inaccuracies in this story. This was pretty much exactly how Hazlehurst explained it to me in 2012, give or take a few stylistic flourishes on my part. He'd been in the 21st Century a year by that point and may have picked up some modern vernacular. Pedants may point out that the Lea Bridge in 1861 was made from iron, not wood, and therefore couldn't have snapped in the manner described, allowing the men to topple into the Navigation. I put this to Hazlehurst and, shrugging, he told me there were far stranger elements to his story than a snapped bridge. He was right. So we left it at that.

Journey to the Rave Hole

The Rave Hole is my own name for the place. I have tagged it. Since I wrote this book, the underpass beneath the intersecting railway bridges behind Walthamstow Marsh no longer hosts graffiti. In another stark example of accelerating change in the Marshland, the curving white walls are now host to 'Mural On the Marsh', an art project created in August 2013, depicting local wildlife. The morning after it was completed, the mural was attacked with gold paint. Anti-graffiti lacquer meant that this attack was short lived. But it shows that the graffiti conversation between competing groups of marsh users is ongoing.

Temples of the Neo Gods

A good source account of the Agapemone cult can be found in Charles Mander's book, *The Reverend Prince And His Abode of Love* (EP Publishing) although I believe it's out of print.

The Ghost Factory

In the mid-70s this factory was where Astrid Proll, getaway driver for the Red Army Faction and member of the Baader-Meinhoff group came to work. Ian Sinclair describes it in his book: *Hackney, That Red Rose Empire* (Penguin).

Biomass

For this story I am indebted to the O'Connell family who allowed me to snoop around their flat in Matchmaker Wharf.

Time's Apostates

In this chapter I describe how the marshland allows people to exit the narrative, away from surveillance cameras, cultural pressures and prying eyes. This also makes them an appealing place to dump bodies. On December 3rd 1980, drug baron and armourer to the Kray twins, Colin 'Duke" Osborne was found dead on Hackney Marshes. The murder remains unsolved.

1.   I owe the phrase and concept 'freedom of narration' to Krzysztof Nawratek, who talks about this in his book *Holes in the Whole: Introduction to The Urban Revolutions* (Zero Books, p.16).

Beasts of the Cryptoforest

Elements of this chapter have been excerpted from 'Monsters of Hackney & Walthamstow Marsh', an essay by the author which appears in *The Ashgate Research Companion to Paranormal Cultures*, edited by Jenzen, O and Munt, S.R (Farnham: Ashgate 2013) pp. 400-403. © 2013

I used a lot of sources for this chapter. If you want to track the bear story for yourself, then you might find these illuminating.

1.   The news report about the police interview with the boys who saw the bear in 1981 is archived on the British Universities Film & Video Council [Online] Available at: http://bufvc.ac.uk/ tvandradio/lbc/index.php/segment/0027600341001   [Accessed 10 April 2012]

2.   Tina Wrath's *Fortean Times* Article, If You Go Down to the Marsh is available at: http://www.forteantimes.com/features/ articles/3415/if_you_go_down_to_the_marsh.html

3.   The quote by W. Hou Je Bek is from this page on his excellent 'Cryptoforestry' website: http://cryptoforest.blogspot. co.uk/p/what-is-cryptoforest.html

Brian's story about the horses' heads on the Lea Bridge can be found on his website, *Tales of the Old East End* http://www.tales-of-the-old-east-end.co.uk/otherstories

Behind the Spectacle

More information about the Lea Valley's industrial history can be found on the Walthamstow Pump House Museum website: http://www.walthamstowpumphousemuseum.org.uk/

The Fires of London

This story was inspired by a track of the same name by The Psychogeographical Commission. You can listen to, and download 'The Fires of London' here:

http://psychcomm.bandcamp.com/track/the-fires-of-london

Endgames

My source for the early part of this chapter is 'Walthamstow: Economic history, marshes and forests', *A History of the County of Essex: Volume 6* (1973), pp. 263-275.
URL: http://www.british-history.ac.uk/report aspx?compid=42779&strquery=lady+day

1.   If you search on YouTube you can hear Katy Andrews' highly detailed lecture about the events of 1892, titled '1892 and all that'.

2.   You can read the full 1979 report WALTHAMSTOW MARSHES: OUR COUNTRYSIDE UNDER THREAT as a PDF on this webpage: http://www.clubplan.org/CMS/usr/20169/ Publications/WalthamstowMarshesSurvey_1970s.PDF
Or you can read it on the Lea Marsh website: http://www. leamarsh.com/1970E17survey/1970E17surveyindex.html

A Dream Life of Hackney Marshes: A Libretto

This is this the complete script of the libretto I wrote for *A Dream Life of Hackney Marshes*, a musical suite composed by the band Jetsam for voice, piano, cello, flute, guitar, bass, keyboards and electronics.

The libretto is based on elements of this book and also my short story of the same title, published in *Acquired for Development By . . .* [Influx Press, 2012] The lyrics for the song section of 'Angel' were co-written and arranged by Sam Mumford.

Jetsam and I performed *A Dream Life of Hackney Marshes* at The Union Chapel, Islington (October 2012), The Vortex Jazz Café, Dalston (January 2013) and the Bishopsgate Institute (March 2013).

A recorded version is available on CD [Claypipe Music].

Jetsam are: Detta Danford, Jo Wills, Sam Mumford, Natasha Zielazinski and Heather Truesdall. Piano is by Eliza McCarthy.

Soundchronicities: Recommended listening

Most of the below are albums and EPs I've taken out onto the marshland to help me experience the topography in new ways. Others are listed because their approach to landscape, memory, decay and the occult has inspired me while writing this book.

- Advisory Circle – *Other Channels* [Ghost Box, 2008]
- Alva Noto – *Xerrox Vol 2* [Raster Norton, 2008]
- Alva Noto & Ryuichi Sakamoto – *UTP_* [Raster Norton, 2009]
- Basic Channel – *BCD* [Basic Channel, 2007]
- William Basinski – *The Disintegration Loops* [Musex International, 2002]
- Broadcast & The Focus Group – *Investigate Witch Cults of the Radio Age* [Warp, 2009]
- The Caretaker – *Persistent Repetition of Phrases* [Install, 2008]
- Wendy Carlos – *Sonic Seasonings* [1972]
- Cloud Waste & The Calf – *Rare Sounds Around Britain Vols 1-3* [2012-2013]
- Clouwbeck – *Wolfrahm* [Shining Day, 2009]
- Coil – *Musick to Play in the Dark* [Trisol, 2003]
- Concretism – *Another Way of Looking At It* [2012]
- Demdike Stare – *Tryptych* [Modern Love, 2011]
- Ekoclef – *Tapeswap* [Magic & Dreams, 2011]
- Ephemeral Man – *Nacreous Clouds* [2013]
- Erstlaub – *Marconi's Shipwreck* [Broken20, 2012]
- Fennesz – *Endless Summer* [Mego, 2001] / *Black Sea* [Touch, 2008]

- The Focus Group – *Hey Let Loose Your Love* [Ghost Box, 2005]
- Lee Gamble – *Diversions 1994-1996* [Pan, 2012]
- Gas – *Konigsforst* [Mille Plateaux, 1999]
- Hacker Farm – *UHF* [Exotic Pylon, 2013]
- Harmonia & Eno '76 – *Tracks and Traces* [Gronland Records, 2009]
- Ryoji Ikeda – *Test Pattern* [Raster Norton, 2008]
- Leyland Kirby – *Eager to Tear Apart the Stars* [History Always Favours the Winners, 2009] / *Sadly The Future is No Longer What it Was* [History Always Favours the Winners, 2011]
- Lost Trail – *A Stained August for the Jetcrash* [Sunup Recordings, 2012] / *The Haunting on Fisher Street* [Tired Sounds, 2012]
- Medroxy Progesterone Acetate – *I Am An Empty House Longing to be Haunted* [Black Horizons, 2012]
- Moon Wiring Club – *An Audience of Art Deco Eyes* [Gecophonic, 2007]
- Machinefabriek – *Weleer* [Lampse, 2007]
- Monolake – *Silence* [Imbalance Computer Music, 2009] / *Ghosts* [Imbalance Computer Music, 2012]
- Mordant Music – *Travelogues 10: Sync Lair* [Mordant Music, 2012] / *Travelogues 11: Reading RheuMatisM* [Mordant Music, 2012]
- Motion Sickness of Time Travel – *Seeping Through the Veil of the Unconscious* [Hooker Vision, 2011]
- Mountains – *Choral* [Thrill Jockey, 2009]

- Oh/ex/oh – *The House in the Woods* [Self-released, 2013]/ *Extant* [The Geography Trip, 2012]
- Oneohtrix Point Never – *Rifts* [No Fun, 2012]
- Pye Corner Audio – *Black Mill Tapes Vol 1&2* [Type Recordings, 2012]
- Pole – *Waldgeshichten* [Pole, 2011]
- Max Richter – *24 Postcards in Full Colour* [Fatcat Records, 2009]
- Shackleton – *Music for the Quiet Hour* [Woe to the Septic Heart, 2012]
- Shackleton/Various – *Soundboy's Gravestone Gets Desecrated by Vandals* [Skull Disco, 2009]
- Stars of the Lid – *And Their Refinement of the Decline* [Kranky, 2008] / *The Tired Sounds of Stars of the Lid* [Kranky, 2001]
- Strangeloop – *Fields* [Brainfeeder, 2011]
- Thanet – *Receiving Calls* [Mordant Music, 2011]
- Time Attendant – *Tournaments* [Exotic Pylon, 2011]
- Wizards Tell Lies – *The Failed Silence* [First Fold Records, 2012]

Acknowledgements

Special thanks to my wife, Emily. To Gary and Kit for encouraging me to write this book. To Ada for the stunning artwork. Top thank-ranking also goes to Dee Dee O'Connell, Jim O'Connell , Rosie O'Connell, Simon Spanton at Gollancz, Caroline Day, David Southwell, Brian Walker, Lindsay Collier, Charlie Tuesday Gates and Jetsam (Detta, Sam, Heather, Jo, Natasha, Eliza).

Thanks to everyone who has supported my marshes project, shared my ideas and inspired my research: Professor Dan Maudlin, Lucy Harrison, Fran Panetta, Nick Laight, John Reppion, Jan Idel, Tina Richardson, Sara Wishart, Bobby Seal, Julian Beere, Wilifred de jou Bek, Matt Barnes, Mark Hollis, Frances Castle, Will Stirling & the gang at *The Dabbler*, the Millfields Blog, Martin Fuller, Matt at The London Report, Owen Booth, John Rogers, Paul Conneally, Nick Edwards, Ralph Cumbers, Jonny Mugwump, Maxim Peter Griffin, Erkembode, Dave Fleet, The Psychogeographical Commission, Fife Psychogeography, Pynchon in Public, Valery Levacher, Martin Cosby, Lucy Fisher, Eddie Proctor, Lines of Landscape, Lost Trail, Hacker Farm, Luke Bennett, Joseph Stannard, Diana Hale, Bill Foster, Tom Chivers, Lee Jackson, Peter Watts, Sara Mohr-Pietsch, Black Classical, The Famulus, Helenography, Julian Cheyne, Jo Roberts, Thomas Hardy, Mauro Thon Giudici, Richard Littler, Leigh Wright, DiL23, Uschi-No-Michi, Kleitia, Jamie Dunning, Bob Seacow, Dan Gusset, Matt Bower, Tim Bird, Andy Welch, Neil Clasper, Julian Hoffman, Fernando Sdrigotti, Eccentronic Research Council, Ken Titmuss, Sally R.Munt, Olu

Jenzen, Tom Bolton, Dave Fyans, Rich Hughes, Scott Wood and that angry bloke who almost beat me up on Walthamstow Marsh for 'ruining Hackney'. Sorry to anyone I forgot.

About the author

Gareth E. Rees is a freelance writer, visiting research fellow at Plymouth University, and author of *The Marshman Chronicles*, a blog about East London's marshes. His short story about a man's love affair with an electricity pylon, 'A Dream Life of Hackney Marshes' appears in the anthology *Acquired for Development By . . .* (Influx Press, 2012).

His spoken word collaboration with the band Jetsam, based on that short story, was performed in venues across East London and released as an album (Clay Pipe Music, 2013).

Rees's cryptozoological essay, 'Monsters of Hackney and Walthamstow Marshes', appears in *The Ashgate Research Companion to Paranormal Cultures* (Ashgate, 2013).

About the illustrator

Born in Sarajevo in 1987, Ada ruined her parents hopes that she'd become a doctor by studying illustration at Westminster University, and then a masters at Kingston just to rub it in.

She currently works as a proffessional scribe and illustrator, motivated by themes which have a social or political relevance, or are just plain macabre.

Previous clients have ranged from Ogilvy to Doctor Clive's Circus; as well as charities and youth initiatives such as Maggie's and The Who Cares Trust. Her work is often featured in the Southbank Centre where she is a resident artist.

www.adajusic.com

Bibliography

Below is a list of works that have inspired me while writing *Marshland*, some not directly referenced but influential on my direction of thought. If you enjoyed this book you should seek out some of these . . .

Local:

The Marshman Chronicles by Gareth E. Rees
http://www.marshmanchronicles.com/

Mapping Your Manor
(featuring an interview with Gareth E. Rees at Eton Manor)
http://mappingyourmanor.com/

Wild Hackney
(an edition of the Hackney Podcast featuring Gareth E. Rees)
http://hackneypodcast.co.uk/2011/07/edition-21-wild-
hackney/

The Hackney Podcast
http://hackneypodcast.co.uk

Lost and Found in E17
http://julianbeere2011.blogspot.co.uk/

Save Lea Marshes
http://saveleytonmarsh.wordpress.com/

Lea Bridge Heritage
http://www.leabridge.org.uk

Lea Marsh
http://www.leamarsh.com/

Millfields Blog
http://millfieldspark.blogspot.co.uk/

Walthamstow Diary

http://walthamstowdiary.com/

Games Monitor

http://www.gamesmonitor.org.uk/

Diamond Geezer

http://diamondgeezer.blogspot.co.uk/

Tales of the Old East End

http://www.tales-of-the-old-east-end.co.uk/

Walthamstow Pump House Museum

http://www.walthamstowpumphousemuseum.org.uk/

Websites about place:

Mythogeography

http://www.mythogeography.com/

Anatomy of Norbiton

http://www.anatomyofnorbiton.org/

The Psychogeographical Commission

http://www.psychetecture.com/

Curiocity

http://www.curiocity.org.uk/

Cryptoforestry

http://cryptoforest.blogspot.co.uk/

Fife Psychogeography

http://fifepsychogeography.wordpress.com/

Other Aberdeen

http://otheraberdeen.blogspot.co.uk/

The Great Wen: A London Blog

http://greatwen.com

The London Fortean Society

http://forteanlondon.blogspot.co.uk/

Liminal London

http://www.liminallondon.com/

Liminal Whitby

http://liminalwhitby.blogspot.co.uk/

Psychogeographic Review

http://psychogeographicreview.com/

Victorian London

http://www.victorianlondon.org/

Scarfolk

http://www.scarfolk.blogspot.de/

Diana J Hale
http://dianajhale.wordpress.com/

The Journal of Wild Culture
http://www.wildculture.com

Caught by the River
http://www.caughtbytheriver.net/

Lines of Landscape
http://linesoflandscape.wordpress.com/

Landscapism
http://landscapism.blogspot.co.uk/

The Hauntological Society
http://thehauntologicalsociety.blogspot.co.uk/

Adventures in Topography (Resonance FM)
http://podcasts.resonancefm.com
page/2?s=ventures+and+adventures+in+topography

Adrift
http://whatisadrift.tumblr.com/

Savage Messiah
http://lauraoldfieldford.blogspot.co.uk/

Derelict London
http://www.derelictlondon.com/

Particulations

http://particulations.blogspot.co.uk/

Luke Bennett

http://lukebennett13.wordpress.com/

London Sound Survey

http://www.soundsurvey.org.uk/

Music :

Gareth E. Rees's marshland music mixes

http://www.mixcloud.com/Hackneymarshman/

Clay Pipe Music

http://www.claypipemusic.co.uk/

The Outer Church

http://theouterchurch.co.uk/

Jetsam

http://www.jetsamsound.com/

Exotic Pylon

http://exoticpylon.com/

Leigh Wright (AKA the Ephemeral Man)

http://leighwright.wordpress.com/

The Geography Trip

http://thegeographytrip.com/

Hacker Farm

http://hackerfarm.net/

Publishing:

Influx Press

http://www.influxpress.com

Avery Hill Publishing

http://www.averyhillpublishing.com/

Lonely Coot

http://lonelycoot.tumblr.com/

Earth Lines

http://www.earthlines.org.uk/

Books:

London, The Biography – Peter Ackroyd (Vintage, 2000)

The Peregrine – J. A Baker (Penguin, 1967)

Stories: Volumes 1 and 2 – Ray Bradbury (Harper Voyager, 2008)

Psychogeography – Merlin Coverley (Pocket Essentials, 2006)

The Art of Wandering: The Writer as Walker – Merlin Coverley (Oldcastle Books, 2012)

Complete Ghost Stories – Charles Dickens
(Wordsworth Classics, 1998)

Edgelands – Paul Farley and Michael Symmons Roberts
(Jonathan Cape, 2011)

Savage Messiah – Laura Oldfield Ford (Verso, 2011)

Neverwhere – Neil Gaiman
(author's preferred text; Headline Review, 2005)

Things That Never Happen – M John Harrison (Gollancz, 2004)

PrairyErth (A Deep Map) – William Least Heat-Moon
(Houghton Miffin, 1991)

The Casebook of Carnacki, the Ghost Finder – William Hope Hodgson
(Wordsworth Editions, 2006)

Blood Rites of the Bourgeoisie – Stewart Home (Book Works, 2010)

Emperors of Dreams: Drugs in the Nineteenth Century – Mike Jay
(Updated and revised edition, Dedalus, 2011)

Necronomicon – H.P. Lovecraft (Gollancz, 2008)

The Unofficial Countryside – Richard Mabey (Little Toller Books,
2010)

The White People and Other Weird Stories – Arthur Machen
(Penguin Classics, 2012)

The Reverend Prince and His Abode of Love – Charles Mander (EP Publishing Ltd, 1976)

The City and the City – China Miéville (Pan, 2011)

Ground Control – Anna Minton (Penguin, 2012)

Holes In The Whole - Krzysztof Nawratek (Zero Books, 2012)

The Lost Art of Walking – Geoff Nicholson (Harbour Books, 2008)

Concrete, Crows and Calluses - Tina Richardson (Particulations Press, 2013)

The Canal – Lee Rourke (Melville House Publishing, 2010)

The Book of Dave – Will Self (Penguin, 2007)

The Cat in the Hat – Dr Seuss (Random House, 1957)

The Rings of Saturn - W.G. Sebald (Vintage, 2002)

Blake's London: The Topographical Sublime – Iain Sinclair (Swedenborg Society, 2011)

Hackney, that Red Rose Empire – Iain Sinclair (Penguin, 2009)

The Meadowlands – Robert Sullivan (Prentice Hall, 1998)

Connecting Nothing with Something -
edited by Gary Budden and Kit Caless
(Influx Press, 2013)

Acquired for Development By . . .
- edited by Gary Budden and Kit Caless
(Influx Press, 2012)

Mind Invaders: A Reader in Psychic Warfare, Cultural Sabotage and Semiotic Terrorism – edited by Stewart Home (Serpent's Tale 1997)

Influx Press is an independent publisher specialising in writing about place.

We publish challenging and alternative work written in order to dissect and analyse our immediate surroundings, to blur genres and to produce site-specific fiction and poetry.

Please visit

www.influxpress.com for extra material, including interviews

and videos with the authors.

Acquired for Development By...

A Hackney Anthology

Twenty-five writers, twenty-five different perspectives on the rapidly changing London Borough of Hackney. From gentrification to supermarket sandwiches, Turkish Alevism to inner-city river living, middle-class civil war to pylon romance, *Acquired for Development By...* captures an alternative, insightful and sometimes bizarre take on modern London life.

'A literary dolly mixture and a superb collection of original writing about London's most fascinating borough. This is Hackney without the hackneyed, and a must-read for anyone who cares about the area.'

– The Londonist

Life in Transit
The Journey that Counts

Sam Berkson

....

Life in Transit searches for the public in a world that is increasingly privatised, both in terms of the 'chartered' space of corporate land grabs, but also the detachment of the individual in the late capitalist experience. Sam Berkson's collection focuses on the journey, rather than the destination.

....

'Berkson's own stories of life spent on London's public transport system bring political meanings to the tawdry and humdrum experience of the everyday commuter.'

– The *Independent*

Connecting Nothing With Something

A Coastal Anthology

Connecting Nothing with Something explores the conflicting and shifting landscape of the south east English coast. Art led regeneration, hidden history, the ghosts of youth culture and the demise of the UK coastal holiday share the page with run-down ferries carrying passengers to the continent, crumbling white cliffs and stolen kisses under the pier.

'The voice is generally sophisticated, sceptical and aloof but also prone to nostalgia and an unspecific sense of loss. Many of the pieces suggest a rapprochement with places almost forgotten about over the last few years, places now indelibly linked with (recently lost) youth.

– Fantastic Journal